TO LIFE!

HEALTHY JEWISH FOOD

TO LIFE!

HEALTHY JEWISH FOOD

HOW TO EAT
FOR
HEALTH & HAPPINESS

JUDI ROSE &
DR **JACKIE ROSE**

INSPIRED BY

EVELYN ROSE

YOUCAXTON
PUBLICATIONS

For our parents, Evelyn and Myer, Margaret and Eric, our husbands, Marc and Alex, Judi's brother Alan and late brother David, and Jackie's sister Josie. And for the next generations, Daniel, Heather, Jamie, Amelia, Erika, Marc, Dani, Josh, Jesse, and Leo, for whom we wish a long and healthy life, filled with happiness and wonderful food.

JUDI ROSE & JACKIE ROSE.
London & Manchester 2020

First published in the UK in 2020
by YouCaxton Publications
youcaxton.co.uk

Published by: YouCaxton Publications 2020

Art Director, Designer & Stylist: Pene Parker

Photographer: Marc Gerstein

Illustrator: Grace Helmer

Food: Judi Rose

Nutrition: Jackie Rose

Nutritional Editor: Len Goldstone

Nutritional Consultant: Eva Lasry-Dome

ISBN: 978-1-913425-06-7

Printed and bound in the UK.

CONTENTS

INTRODUCTION

Evelyn Rose, the doyenne of Anglo Jewish cooking, was often asked, "What exactly is Jewish food?" to which she would reply "It's food that Jews eat."

From cuisines and cultures across the world, Jewish mothers have handed down recipes to the next generation, inspired by local cuisine and ingredients, adapted to conform with kashrut – Jewish dietary laws. As circumstances, times, and tastes changed, Jewish food has evolved. This book we hope will continue that tradition.

Many traditional Jewish dishes, particularly those from Eastern Europe, rightly deserve their reputation for being stodgy and unhealthy. Developed to sustain our forebears through long harsh winters, they are high in fat, sugar, salt, and white carbs, which we now know increase the risk of heart disease, diabetes, stroke and cancer. To make matters worse, many of us do little or no physical work and those of Ashkenazi descent are at higher risk for inherited conditions like Coeliac or Crohn's disease.

In many ways, it's now easier than ever to eat healthily. We have access to ingredients our grandparents could scarcely have imagined. Sephardi and new Israeli cuisine with their emphasis on fresh fruit and vegetables have become enormously popular. We have the internet.

News of the latest miracle diet, superfood, or cancer risk assails us almost every day. But much of this seems confusing or contradictory, so it's tempting just to stick to foods we know and love. Our goal in this book is to help you make healthy choices with confidence, based on evidence-based medical and nutritional research, while still enjoying the glorious dishes that make up Jewish food from Israel and the Diaspora.

As busy professionals, wives and mothers, we know that however healthy a recipe is, unless it's easy to make, looks and tastes delicious, and really works, it's unlikely to become a family favourite. So we've filled this book with recipes inspired by the great Evelyn Rose that we think meet those criteria, and that we love to cook and share. We hope you'll love them too.

As Evelyn Rose used to say, enjoy them in good health.

HOW TO USE THE RECIPES

OVEN TEMPERATURES & COOKING TIMES

These are given in degrees Celsius and gas number(°C/Gas.) Unless otherwise noted, ovens are assumed to be using conventional heat. Follow the manufacturer's guidelines for fan-assisted ovens. Conventional and microwave ovens vary in performance and efficiency, as do electric hobs or gas stoves, so cooking times given should be used as guidelines only.

STORAGE TIMES

Recommended storage times for each recipe are based on the maximum period during which the food is pleasant and safe to eat and are based on the following assumptions.

Refrigerated foods are stored in airtight containers, or covered with cling film or foil to avoid dehydration and the transference of flavours and smells from one food to another.

Frozen foods, whether cooked or raw, are stored in airtight containers, freezer storage bags or foil packages to prevent freezer 'burn'. The recommended storage time is based on the maximum period after which deterioration of flavour or texture may take place. If frozen for longer, they shouldn't be dangerous to eat, but will be past their prime.

SUGAR & SUGAR SUBSTITUTES

In most recipes, we've either omitted or at least halved the amount of sugar in the original, relying on fruit or vegetables to provide natural sweetness. In a few cases, we've added back some of the sweetness to cakes in the form of erythritol, a plant-based sugar substitute.

Current research suggests that erythritol is one of the safest sugar substitutes. It has fewer digestive side effects than xylitol, a chemically similar sweetener, and less of an after-taste than stevia. Unlike honey or coconut sugar, erythritol does not cause a spike in blood sugar, and contains negligible calories. Unlike agave, it has no fructose, a fruit sugar which can increase unhealthy abdominal fat.

One rounded teaspoon of erythritol is about as sweet as one level teaspoon of sugar. As your sensitivity to sweetness increases, you'll find you can use less of either, especially in cakes and desserts.

GLUTEN-FREE

VEGAN

1 tsp = 1 level teaspoon or 5 ml
1 tbsp = 1 level tablespoon or 15 ml
1 handful = about half a cup or 125 ml (4 fl oz)
1 pinch = about ⅛ teaspoon

INGREDIENTS & MEASUREMENTS

Several recipes which contain eggs, fish, meat, or dairy can be easily adapted for vegans or vegetarians and include suggestions on how to do so.

Unless otherwise specified, herbs are fresh, flour is plain, sugar is granulated, pepper is freshly ground, and salt is fine sea salt that we think tastes much better than regular table salt. Milk is whole or semi-skimmed. Parmesan may be substituted with any Italian-style hard cheese.

Less common ingredients are explained in the Glossary on page 11.

Pregnant women, infants, the elderly, anyone with an impaired immune system or convalescing from an illness are advised to avoid raw eggs and cured fish. Pregnant women should also avoid liver.

Both metric and Imperial measures are given. They are not interchangeable, however, so follow either one or the other.

Values for calories (cals) and grams of carbohydrates (g carbs) are approximate and are not guaranteed for diabetic calculations.

SEASONING

Taste is subjective, so some of the recipes include instructions to "check the seasoning." If it doesn't taste quite right to you, adding between a pinch and half a teaspoon of fine sea salt and three to five grinds of black pepper usually solves the problem.

CULINARY GLOSSARY

Aleppo Pepper Fairly mild dried chilli pepper with a warm, rich flavour reminiscent of sundried tomatoes.

Casserole Lidded two-handled metal, Pyrex, or ceramic oven proof pan or container. Flameproof or stovetop casseroles can be used on a gas or electric stove. Also a stew cooked in a casserole.

Dried Mushrooms These add a rich, deep flavour to dishes. For the best flavour, use a mix that includes porcini. Soak before using. The well-strained soaking liquid can also be used.

Fond The flavourful residue left on the bottom of the pan after browning chicken or meat. Often incorporated into a sauce by adding liquid.

Gratin or Baking Dish An oval or rectangular oven-proof metal or ceramic dish, usually no more than 7 cm (3") deep.

Ground Flaxseed Rich in omega-3, this is milled from brown or golden flaxseed, also known as linseed. The golden variety looks more attractive in most dishes.

Mirin Slightly sweet Japanese rice wine. May contain sugar, so use sparingly.

Miso Savoury Japanese paste made from fermented soya beans. Sold in the chilled section of supermarkets. White, or shiro, miso is milder and less salty than brown miso.

Nigella Seeds Small black triangular seeds often sprinkled on flatbreads. When roasted or baked, they have a herby, slightly peppery taste. Also called black onion seeds, kalonji, or charnushka.

Oat Bran The outer layer of oat grains. Higher in protein and fibre than rolled or breakfast oats.

Pearled Spelt An ancient grain, mentioned in the Bible. The outer layer of bran is removed, making it easier to cook. Substitute pearl barley.

Pulse To mix ingredients in a food processor or blender in a series of short bursts. Also, the dried seeds of legumes such as beans, peas, or lentils.

Ras el Hanout A Middle Eastern spice blend. The name means "top of the shop". Some versions contain up to 30 different spices, including ginger, cinnamon, pepper, cloves, coriander, cardamom, and dried rosebuds.

Sauté Pan A wide, deep frying pan, usually about 30 cm (12") diameter to make it easier to toss food without spilling it.

Sauté To toss small pieces of food in the air while frying by jerking the pan so they brown on all sides. From the French sauter, to jump.

Shichimi Togarashi Japanese spice mix of chillies and sesame seeds. Equal parts of chilli flakes, black and white sesame seeds may be used instead.

Simmer To gently bubble liquids and sauces just below boiling point.

Soy sauce Available as light, dark, and tamari. Light soy can be salty, so use a low sodium variety if possible. Dark soy adds a deep rich flavour but may contain caramel so use sparingly. Tamari contains little or no wheat, so often gluten-free.

Spelt Flour Available in white and wholemeal, spelt flour has more protein and has a lower glycaemic index (GI) than wheat flour.

Stir Fry To toss or scoop bite-sized pieces of vegetables or protein in a small amount of oil over high heat, usually in a wok.

Sumac Middle Eastern berry with a sharp lemony flavour, sold as a coarse purple powder.

Yuzu juice From an oriental citrus fruit. Tastes like a mix of grapefruit, lime and tangerine.

Za'atar Middle Eastern seasoning, a mix of wild thyme (za'atar), sesame seeds, sumac, and salt.

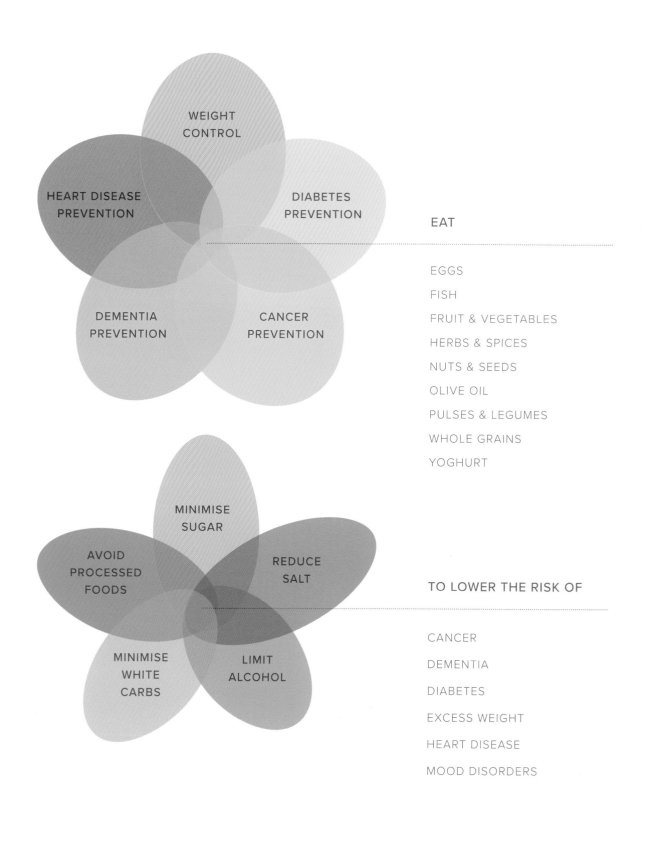

WEIGHT
CONTROL

HEART DISEASE
PREVENTION

DIABETES
PREVENTION

DEMENTIA
PREVENTION

CANCER
PREVENTION

EAT

EGGS

FISH

FRUIT & VEGETABLES

HERBS & SPICES

NUTS & SEEDS

OLIVE OIL

PULSES & LEGUMES

WHOLE GRAINS

YOGHURT

MINIMISE
SUGAR

AVOID
PROCESSED
FOODS

REDUCE
SALT

MINIMISE
WHITE
CARBS

LIMIT
ALCOHOL

TO LOWER THE RISK OF

CANCER

DEMENTIA

DIABETES

EXCESS WEIGHT

HEART DISEASE

MOOD DISORDERS

HEALTHIER EATING

HOW TO GET STARTED

The medieval physician and scholar, Maimonides (the Rambam) counselled that to eat a healthier diet you must change your habits not just your food.

As twenty-first century food lovers, cooks, mothers and wives embarking on our own journey to cook and eat healthier food for ourselves and those we love, we have found this to be good advice. It also takes patience and determination, especially if there's a sceptical spouse in the picture who likes their food "just the way it is, thank you very much," or kids with a "nosh" habit and disdain for all things vegetable other than chips and roasties.

The Rambam recommended starting slowly, making many small changes over time, rather than sudden drastic ones. So take things slowly, be kind to yourself and don't feel guilty about taking short cuts, like buying ready-peeled vegetables and pre-cooked pulses. To be honest, it's taken us well over a year to reach the point where we prefer brown spaghetti to white, and find sugary food unpleasantly sweet.

A bit of stealth may come in handy too. Perhaps you use half the usual amount of sugar in one of your family's favourite recipes. Or throw a handful of spinach or kale in your meatballs and replace matzah meal with porridge oats. Perhaps you have a meatless main once or twice a week, or experiment with beans and pulses in soups and sides.

Even though it's now clear that excess sugar is bad for our health, as food-lovers we know it's not realistic to cut out all sugar for the rest of one's life. So our recipes are low sugar but not sugar-free versions of traditional dishes. If you live with diabetes, they're easily adapted by substituting a diabetic-friendly sweetener. Some also include butter, white flour, potatoes, or crème fraîche, but you should of course feel free to adapt them to suit your own dietary needs.

The following pages will give you an overview of the best foods to eat, and you can read a more detailed explanation of the interaction between diet and health later in the book. We hope this will make it easier for you to plan, cook, and enjoy healthy, delicious meals.

EAT MORE

FRUIT & VEGETABLES

Fruit and vegetables are vital for good health, and integral to the Mediterranean diet. They're loaded with vitamins and antioxidants that help the body's natural defences, and reduce the risk of chronic diseases such as diabetes, cancer, heart disease, and dementia. Eating a wide range of different fruit and vegetables maximises their benefits, and is a safer way of getting vitamins and antioxidants than taking supplements.

WHOLE GRAINS

These reduce the absorption of cholesterol in food. They're also high in B vitamins, folic acid, and fibre to promote good gut bacteria for digestive and general health. The more processed the grains are, the less well they work, so they need to remain whole to be most effective.

HEALTHY FATS

Oils that may improve your health include extra virgin olive oil and cold-pressed rapeseed oil. Cold-pressed or organic oils are usually more natural, undamaged, and keep more of their antioxidants. Oily fish, avocados, nuts, and seeds are also great sources of healthy fats. Certain fats, including coconut oil and rapeseed oil, are relatively safe for cooking at higher temperatures because of their high smoke point, which makes them less prone to break down into harmful compounds when heated.

FISH, CHICKEN & EGGS

These are all good sources of high-quality protein, vitamins, and iron. Oily fish is rich in healthy fats, and may reduce the risk of heart disease, cancer, and dementia. If possible, buy wild-caught rather than farmed fish. Chicken and eggs have little effect on blood cholesterol in most people. Eggs, especially the yolks, are a nutritional powerhouse, and are rich in vitamin D for healthy bones.

LEGUMES & PULSES

Legumes are starchy vegetables grown in pods, including beans, peas and chickpeas. Pulses are dried seeds of legumes, such as lentils. These all lower cholesterol and help prevent diabetes and dementia. They are a key part of the diet in communities with exceptional longevity, known as Blue Zones.

BERRIES

These are particularly high in potent antioxidants known as anthocyanins. Berries are less likely to raise the blood sugar than many other fruits, and have a reputation for helping to prevent Alzheimer's disease.

HERBS, SPICES & SALAD DRESSINGS

Fresh herbs and spices can aid digestion, fight inflammation, and be wonderful sources of antioxidants. Homemade unsweetened salad dressings made with healthy fats such as extra virgin olive oil, are also high in antioxidants, and help absorb the vitamins in vegetables and salad greens.

NUTS & SEEDS

These are high in heart-healthy monounsaturated fat and essential fatty acids, vitamin E, and zinc. Nuts also contain arginine that helps improve the circulation. They're a great choice for a healthy snack or pick-me-up.

DAIRY PRODUCTS

Recent research suggests that for most people, eating dairy products in moderation does not have an adverse effect on the heart or general health. They are rich in nutrients including protein, calcium, vitamins and antioxidants and may help to reduce the risk of diabetes, stroke, and osteoporosis. Butter, cream, and cheese are also high in saturated fats, so these should only be eaten in moderation.

LIVE OR BIO NATURAL YOGHURT

This acts as a probiotic, boosting your good gut bacteria, helping immunity, reducing inflammation, and protecting against heart disease and cancer. Other fermented foods including sauerkraut, kombucha (fermented tea) and kefir have similar benefits. Eating unsweetened natural yoghurt every day has also been shown to reduce the risk of osteoporosis.

EAT LESS

REFINED & HIGHLY PROCESSED OMEGA-6 OILS

Omega-6 is found in sunflower oil, corn oil, groundnut oil, soya oil, and cottonseed oil. Unfortunately, these are usually refined or highly processed. A moderate amount of omega-6 is healthy and can help your cholesterol profile, but is best obtained by eating whole foods such as nuts, seeds, eggs, and dairy products. If consumed frequently, refined omega-6 oils may be a risk for inflammation. They also interfere with the benefits of omega-3, and can form unhealthy by-products when used for frying at high-temperatures, especially if the oil is used more than once.

RED MEAT

Lean red meat is a good source of iron, B vitamins, and protein, including all the essential amino acids. For most people it is fine to eat some fresh red meat, especially if grass-fed. However, it is recommended you eat no more than 70 grams (cooked weight) per day, and have a few meat-free days each week to reduce the risk of high cholesterol and bowel cancer.

SALT

Some salt is needed in our diet, especially in hot weather to replace what we lose through sweating. However, excess salt can raise blood pressure and increase the risk of suffering a stroke. Most of the salt in our diet is "invisible" as it comes from processed food. The current recommendation is for just 6 grams or 1 teaspoon per day.

MINIMISE

SUGAR

Eating too much sugar – more than 28 grams (1 oz) a day – is a risk for coronary artery disease, including angina, and is one of the main causes of obesity and type 2 diabetes. Linked with these may be an increased risk for raised blood pressure, fatty liver, raised LDL (bad) cholesterol, stroke, cancer, and dementia.

ALCOHOL

Alcohol can have a similar though even worse impact on the metabolism than sugar. Over-drinking can also detrimentally affect your mood and sleep as well as your physical health, and is a risk for cancer, diabetes and dementia. Drinking up to one small glass of red wine a day may, however, be good for the heart.

PROCESSED MEAT

If eaten frequently, deli meats, saveloys, sausages, and salami raise your bad (LDL) cholesterol and risk of diabetes and cancer. They often contain high levels of sugar, salt, white carbs, and preservatives, and are classed as carcinogenic by the World Health Organisation.

OTHER PROCESSED FOODS

Many processed foods and "nosh", especially snacks, pies, cakes and biscuits, are high in sugar, salt and unhealthy fats. This is a particularly unhealthy combination and a risk for raised cholesterol, heart disease, and obesity. They may also contain preservatives, gelling agents, emulsifiers, and other chemical additives.

TRANSFATS

Often labelled "partially hydrogenated fats" these are harmful to the heart and should be avoided. A staple of junk food for decades, they have mostly been removed from foods in the UK, EU and USA, but it is important to check the label, especially on imported baked goods.

WHITE CARBS

These include refined carbohydrates such as white flour, white bread, plain pasta, white rice, sugar, and white potatoes. When eaten, they cause a rapid spike in blood sugar levels, which then causes a spike in insulin. Eating too many white carbs can be a risk for diabetes, obesity, heart disease, and some forms of cancer. Replacing them with healthier complex carbohydrates like wholemeal flour, wholegrain bread, brown rice, and sweet potatoes provides numerous health benefits. Portion sizes for even these healthier carbs should be limited, especially in pre-diabetes and diabetes, to achieve better blood sugar control.

THE MEDITERRANEAN DIET

When British tourists first visited the Costa Brava in the 1960s, they were unfamiliar with the lightly cooked vegetables, salads, and above all, the liberal amounts of extra virgin olive oil used in everything from soups to stews. They labelled Spanish cuisine "greasy". Little did they realise that when it came to healthy eating, Mediterranean cooks were well ahead of their time.

The Mediterranean diet has been studied extensively and has been shown to have excellent health credentials, especially for the prevention of type 2 diabetes and coronary heart disease. One of the world's longest-running nutrition studies, the PREDIMED Study (Prevención con Dieta Mediterránea) has demonstrated that the Mediterranean diet reduces the risk of heart disease by about a third, and improves longevity. There is growing evidence that regularly eating a Mediterranean diet also reduces the risk of dementia.

At its heart is the idea of eating whole grains, a rainbow of fruit and vegetables, plenty of extra virgin olive oil, nuts and seeds high in healthy fats, fresh herbs and spices, fish rather than meat, a moderate amount of legumes, pulses, and dairy foods, especially yoghurt, some poultry, and a limited amount of red meat and red wine. It's not unlike the Israeli kibbutz diet. Eating like an Israeli Sabra will not only connect you with the land, but also keep you healthy in mind and body.

The modern Mediterranean diet has evolved over time, and the most up to date recommendations include drinking eight glasses of water a day, and herbal infusions such as fresh mint in hot water. Lifestyle changes like getting enough sleep, eating with friends and family rather than "on the go" or alone, and using fresh seasonal and local produce are also included.

There's now a trend toward a low carb version of the Med diet, in which all forms of carbohydrate, including whole grains, are reduced though not entirely excluded. Fibre, from plentiful fruit and vegetables, nuts, and seeds, is, however, included.

Being largely plant-based, the Mediterranean diet is also great for vegetarians and vegans, and tends to be more economical and environmentally friendly. Nor do you need to buy expensive superfoods sourced from distant countries, or be on a highly restricted diet to stay in good physical and mental health.

As you'll see, the advice and recipes in this book are a kosher twist on the new Mediterranean diet that are also low in sugar and white carbs. We've found this approach to healthy eating easy to follow and to stick to. Most importantly, the long term benefits can be life-changing.

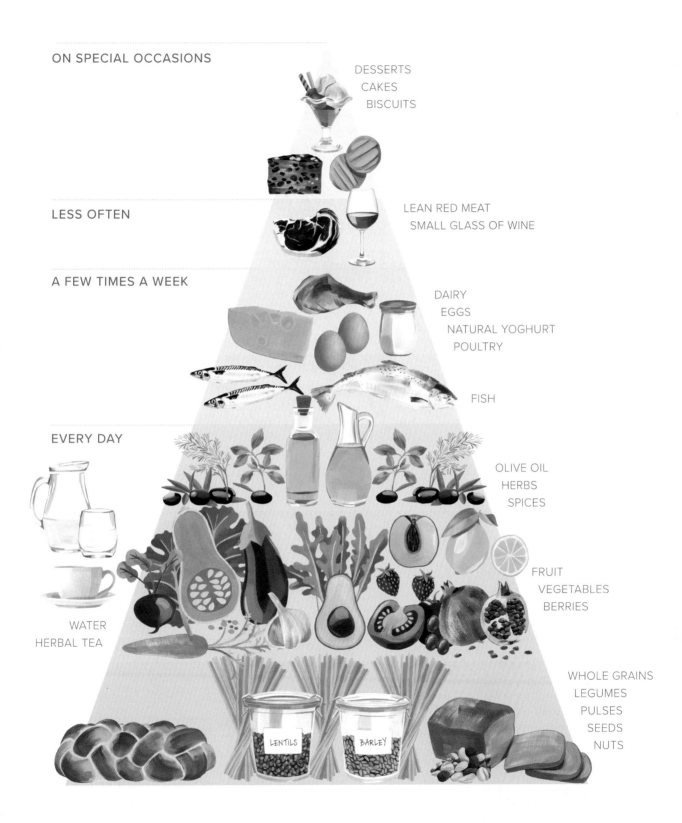

ON SPECIAL OCCASIONS

DESSERTS
CAKES
BISCUITS

LESS OFTEN

LEAN RED MEAT
SMALL GLASS OF WINE

A FEW TIMES A WEEK

DAIRY
EGGS
NATURAL YOGHURT
POULTRY

FISH

EVERY DAY

OLIVE OIL
HERBS
SPICES

FRUIT
VEGETABLES
BERRIES

WATER
HERBAL TEA

WHOLE GRAINS
LEGUMES
PULSES
SEEDS
NUTS

LENTILS   BARLEY

DAILY PHYSICAL ACTIVITY & EATING WITH FAMILY & FRIENDS

1 | SOUPS

MOROCCAN LENTIL SOUP

Serves: 6-8
Keeps: 3 days in the fridge
Freeze: 3 months
Per serving: 175 cals, 30 g carbs

A vibrant Sephardi-inspired soup, fragrant with warm spices and fresh ginger. Lentils are great for heart health, lowering your cholesterol, and stabilising blood sugar levels. They're also incredibly high in protein and fibre. Tomatoes are rich in lycopene that may help reduce the risk of cancer and osteoporosis.

1 large onion
1 large red pepper
2 tbsp olive oil
1 tsp cumin seeds
3 large cloves of garlic
280 g (10 oz) red or orange lentils
4 cm (1½") piece fresh ginger
1 rounded tsp ground coriander
400 g tin chopped tomatoes
1 tsp sea salt
15 grinds black pepper
2 litres (3½ pints) vegetable
   stock made with 3-4 cubes

To serve
extra virgin olive oil
1-2 tsp roasted cumin seeds
fresh parsley

Halve, peel then finely chop the onion and the trimmed, seeded red pepper. Heat the oil in a soup pan with the onion, pepper, cumin and a pinch of salt, followed by the garlic, crushed in a press. Cook gently, covered, for 8-10 minutes, stirring once or twice.

Meanwhile, rinse the lentils in a large sieve until the water runs clear (this makes them easier to digest). Peel and grate the ginger, then add to the pan with the coriander. Cook for another minute then add the lentils, tomatoes, seasonings, and stock. Simmer, covered, for an hour.

Leave to cool for the flavour to develop then chill, freeze, or reheat until bubbling. Serve with a drizzle of extra virgin olive oil, a sprinkle of roasted cumin seeds, and a dash of parsley.

SRI LANKAN LENTIL SOUP

Add ½ teaspoon ground turmeric and ½ teaspoon chilli powder with the grated ginger and use only 1.5 litres (2 ½ pints) stock.

After simmering for an hour, turn off the heat and whisk in a well-shaken 400 g tin of reduced-fat coconut milk. Top each serving with a few coriander or parsley leaves and serve with wedges of fresh lime to squeeze into the soup.

JUDI'S TIPS: an easy way to peel a knobbly piece of ginger is to scrape the skin off as much as you need from one end of the root using a metal tablespoon, leaving the rest unpeeled for future use. Tinned tomatoes vary in acidity, so if the finished soup tastes too sharp, add a pinch of cane sugar or erythritol to balance the flavour.

MYER'S WINTER VEGETABLE SOUP WITH BASIL INFUSED CROUTONS

Serves: 6-8
Keeps: 2 days in the fridge
Freeze: 3 months
Per serving: 160 cals, 27 g carbs

This satisfying soup makes the most of winter produce, while its Mediterranean flavours are a reminder of warmer days. It's high in fibre, vitamins A and C for liver health, and a great way to help children get their five-a-day. Savoy cabbage is particularly high in potentially cancer-fighting compounds. Both the soup and croutons can be made several days ahead and freeze well.

---

2 medium red onions
2 tbsp olive oil
2 small carrots
2 small potatoes
1 stick of celery
1 courgette
1 medium leek
2 tbsp tomato purée
400 g tin chopped tomatoes
1.7 litres (3 pints) strong
   vegetable stock
225 g (8 oz) fresh
   or frozen green beans
225 g tin cannellini
   or haricot beans
handful of finely shredded
   Savoy cabbage
1 tsp dried Italian mixed herbs
   or oregano
3 tbsp frozen peas
½-1 tsp fine sea salt
10 grinds black pepper

For the croutons
3 slices brown bread
2 tbsp extra virgin olive oil
handful fresh basil leaves
pinch of salt

To serve
handful of fresh basil leaves
grated parmesan

Peel and finely chop the onions. Heat the oil in a large soup pan (2.25 litre/4 pint) and gently cook the onions with a pinch of salt, covered, for 8-10 minutes until soft, stirring occasionally.

Meanwhile, chop the peeled carrots, unpeeled potatoes, and the topped and tailed celery, leek, and courgette into 1 cm (½") cubes.

When the onions are soft, stir in the tomato purée, chopped vegetables, tomatoes, and stock. Cover and simmer for 15 minutes.

Trim the green beans then cut them into 2 cm (1½") pieces. Drain and thoroughly rinse the tinned beans (this makes them easier to digest). Now add the beans and all the remaining soup ingredients to the pan and simmer, uncovered, for 8-10 minutes or until the vegetables are tender. Taste the soup, adding more pepper or sea salt if needed.

For the croutons, preheat the oven to 180°C/Gas 4. Cut the sliced bread into 1 cm (½") cubes. Purée the oil, basil and salt in a mini food processor or pound to a rough paste with a mortar and pestle. Toss the cubes of bread with the basil oil, then spread them on a large baking sheet. Bake for 10-15 minutes, shaking once or twice, until the croutons are crisp and golden brown. To serve, bring the soup to a simmer, add the roughly chopped basil leaves, and serve with the croutons and parmesan.

JUDI'S TIP: parmesan rinds add a wonderful savoury, nutty flavour to tomato-based soups, so whenever you finish a piece of Parmesan, freeze the rind. When making your soup, throw a piece or two into the pot with the stock. Once cooked, the rind becomes edible and quite delicious. To turn the soup into a one-pot meal, add a handful of wholemeal pasta during the last 10-15 minutes of cooking.

WILD ROCKET SOUP WITH MINT & PETITS POIS

Serves: 6-8
Keeps: 3 days in the fridge
Freeze: 3 months
Per serving: 135 cals, 16 g carbs

A lovely jade green soup that's quick and easy to make. It can also be served chilled like its sorrel-based East European cousin, schav. As a child, Evelyn Rose used to help her Latvian-born grandmother forage for wild sorrel on the local golf course. If you happen to have some growing in your garden or come across it in a shop, mix a handful with the rocket or spinach.

The soup is packed with fibre and vitamins, great for healthy skin, energy, and immunity. Crunchy pine nuts, which are rich in heart-healthy monounsaturated fat, add a delicious finishing touch and can be toasted several days ahead.

---

1 large onion

2 tbsp extra virgin olive oil

850 ml (1 ½ pints) strong vegetable stock

450 g (1 lb) frozen petits pois

½ -1 tsp fine sea salt

1 small bunch fresh mint

225 g (8 oz) wild rocket or baby spinach

3 tbsp pine nuts

10 grinds black pepper

Finely chop the onion. Heat the olive oil and onion in a soup pan with a pinch of salt, and cook gently, covered, for 8-10 minutes, until soft and golden, stirring occasionally. Add the stock, peas, and salt, bring to the boil and cook, covered, until the peas are tender, about 5 minutes.

Remove the coarse stalks from the mint and set aside a few sprigs for serving. Add the rocket or spinach and mint to the pan, then simmer for 3 minutes, uncovered to preserve the lovely green colour. Purée in a blender until absolutely smooth (a food processor also works but the texture won't be quite so creamy). If possible, leave the soup to cool for half an hour or so for the flavour to develop.

Toast the pine nuts in an empty non-stick pan over gentle heat, shaking often, until golden on all sides, 3-5 minutes or on a baking sheet in the oven at 180°C/Gas 4 for 10 minutes, shaking the baking sheet halfway through.

To serve hot, bring the soup back to a simmer, add the black pepper, then taste and re-season if necessary. If the soup is very thick, add a little stock or hot water until it's the consistency of whipping cream. Serve sprinkled with pine nuts and the reserved mint leaves.

WINTER BORSCHT

Serves: 6-8
Keeps: 2 days in the fridge
Freeze: 3 months
Per serving: 78 cals, 18 g carbs

The unique sweet and sour flavour of this iconic Russian Jewish soup is traditionally achieved with citric acid and lots of sugar. Our version relies almost entirely on the natural sweetness of the vegetables, and the tang of fresh lemon juice. Rather than discarding the vegetables after cooking, we purée them with the broth to produce fibre-rich soup that needs no eggs to thicken it.

For the prettiest colour, use a white or purple-fleshed sweet potato. Adding half a red onion boosts the flavour, but remove it before puréeing the other vegetables or it will spoil the lovely smooth texture of the finished soup. For the best flavour, make the borscht ahead and chill or freeze until needed.

---

2 bunches of young beets,
　　or 900g (2 lb) old beets

1 medium sweet potato

1 medium carrot

1.6 litres (28 fl oz) strong
　　vegetable stock

15 grinds of black pepper

1 tsp fine sea salt

2-3 tsp caster sugar or erythritol

1-2 tbsp fresh lemon juice

You'll need a large (2 litre/4 pint) soup pan. Top, tail and peel the vegetables, then cut them into chunks and process in two batches in the food processor until very finely chopped. Transfer to the pan and add the stock, pepper, and salt, and the red onion if using.

Bring to the boil, cover, and simmer for 20 minutes until the vegetables are very soft and the liquid is a rich, dark red. Remove the onion if used.

Purée the rest of the vegetables and the liquid in a blender (in 2 batches if necessary) until absolutely smooth, then add the lemon juice and sugar or sweetener. Taste and adjust the seasoning, adding more lemon juice or sugar as needed so you have a lovely balance of sweet and sour.

SUMMER BORSCHT

Chilled on the rocks, this makes a wonderful summer starter.

Make exactly as for winter borscht, then chill thoroughly. Just before serving, whisk in 150 ml (5 fl oz) of Greek yoghurt, soured cream, or fromage frais. Fill 6-8 wine glasses or tumblers one-third full with ice cubes and top up with the chilled borscht.

JUDI'S TIPS: beetroot leaves a purple calling card on everything it touches, so I avoid wooden cutting boards and wear disposable gloves when handling it. After transferring the chopped veggies to the pan, swirl a little water around the bowl of the food processor to catch any bits left behind then add to the stock.

TUSCAN BEAN SOUP WITH CAVOLO NERO

Serves: 4-6
Keeps: 3 days in the fridge
Freeze: 3 months
Per serving: 210 cals, 31 g carbs

A richly flavoured soup from the hills of Tuscany. Its flavour is best if made several hours ahead and reheated just before serving. Cavolo nero, also known as Tuscan black kale, has a milder, nuttier flavour than its British cousin, curly kale.

2 medium carrots

1 stick celery

1 medium leek

2 tbsp extra virgin olive oil

1 tsp fresh rosemary
    or ½ tsp dried rosemary

1 tsp fennel seeds

2 cloves garlic

1 tbsp tomato purée

½-1 tsp sea salt

2 x 400 g tin cannellini
    or haricot beans

1 litre (35fl oz) strong
    vegetable stock

100g (3 ½ oz) cavolo nero,
    or a handful of baby spinach
    or chopped curly kale

10 grinds black pepper

extra virgin olive oil to serve

Trim, peel and chop the carrots and celery into small dice by hand or food processor. Trim then quarter the white part of the leek lengthwise and slice thinly. Strip fresh rosemary leaves from the stalk and chop finely.

Heat the oil, rosemary and fennel seeds in a soup pan for 30 seconds until fragrant, then add the garlic, crushed in a press, tomato purée, and chopped vegetables. Sprinkle with the salt, and stir to coat with the fragrant oil. Rinse and drain the beans, then add to the pan with the stock and simmer for 15-20 minutes or until the vegetables are soft.

Strip the cavolo nero leaves from the coarse stalks (save the stalks for vegetable stock if you like). Roll the leaves up into a tight bundle then shred coarsely. Add to the pan and simmer, uncovered, until tender, about 5 minutes.

Remove a ladleful of the beans with some of the liquid, purée it until smooth in a blender or food processor, then return the purée to the pan. Stir in the black pepper. Leave to cool for the flavour to develop. To serve, reheat, until bubbling, and top each serving with a drizzle of extra virgin olive oil.

CAVOLO NERO AND KALE, like all cruciferous vegetables such as broccoli, cabbage, cauliflower, and sprouts, can help reduce the risk of cancer. They're particularly high in antioxidants, iron, vitamins A, B, C, E and K, and offer protection against osteoporosis.

KRUPNIK WILD MUSHROOM & BARLEY SOUP

NOT GLUTEN FREE

Serves: 6-8
Keeps: 4 days in the fridge
Freeze: 3 months
Per serving: 110 cals, 18 g carbs

Krupnik was a mainstay of Jewish cooking in Poland, where wild mushrooms grew plentifully in the woods and meadows, foraged in autumn, then dried and used in soups and stews over the long, cold winter. Dried mushrooms add a wonderful flavour, but if not available, use a handful of fresh shiitake or other wild mushrooms.

handful dried wild mushrooms
  (see page 11)

1 large onion

2 tbsp olive oil

1 large carrot

1 medium leek

125 g (4 oz) pearl barley
  or quick-cook barley

1 bay leaf

4 sprigs of parsley

4 sprigs of snipped fresh dill,
  or 1 tsp dried dill

2 litres (3 ½ pints) vegetable
  or chicken stock

300 g (10 oz) chestnut mushrooms

½ tsp fine sea salt

generous pinch white pepper

10 grinds black pepper

Soak the dried mushrooms in boiling water for 20 minutes. Line a sieve with a paper towel and set it over a jug or bowl. Add the soaked mushrooms to the sieve and strain the liquid into the jug. Remove the paper towel, rinse the mushrooms under running water to remove any remaining sand or grit then add them to the filtered liquid in the jug. Cover the pearl barley with boiling water.

Finely chop the onion then cook it in 1 tablespoon of the oil and a pinch of salt in a large 3.5 litre (6 pint) soup pan, covered for the first 5 minutes, until soft and golden, 8 -10 minutes.

While the onion cooks, peel the carrot, trim the leek, then chop both finely either by hand or food processor. Drain the barley. Add the vegetables and barley to the pan with the stock, parsley, bay leaf, and the dried mushrooms with their strained soaking liquid. Cover and simmer until the barley is soft, 10 minutes for quick-cook barley, 40-50 minutes for regular pearl barley.

While the soup is cooking, slice the fresh mushrooms thinly and sauté them with the remaining oil in a large frying pan until a rich brown. Add them to the soup with the dill and seasonings. Leave to mature for several hours or overnight, then remove the parsley (don't worry about the bay leaf). Or freeze until needed.

To serve, reheat until bubbling. If the soup has thickened too much on standing, add some more stock or boiling water. If previously frozen, add a handful of snipped dill to perk up the flavour.

BARLEY AND MUSHROOMS contain selenium, an antioxidant with cancer-fighting properties. Like all whole grains, barley is high in fibre — great for lowering LDL cholesterol — and magnesium, which helps lower blood pressure. It also contains niacin, one of the B vitamins that boosts your mood, perhaps why barley so often features in comfort foods.

AUTUMN SQUASH SOUP
WITH CITRUS & GINGER

Serves: 6-8
Keeps: 3 days in the fridge
Freeze: 2 months
Per serving: 90 cals, 18 g carbs

A lovely golden soup with a refreshing flavour. We like to top each serving with frizzled ginger, croutons, or Greek yoghurt. Squash is high in vitamin A, which is good for night vision, reducing the risk of cataracts and macular degeneration.

900g (2 lb) butternut squash
1 medium onion
2 cloves of garlic
2 sticks of celery
2 tbsp extra virgin olive oil
3 tbsp grated fresh ginger
1.5 litres (2 ½ pints) strong
  vegetable stock
1 large orange
2 tsp fresh lime juice
½ tsp fine sea salt
10 grinds black pepper

For the frizzled ginger
5 cm (2") piece of fresh ginger
2 tsp olive, coconut
  or rapeseed oil

To make the squash easier to peel and cut, microwave it for 2-3 minutes, or bake in the oven for 10 minutes. When cool enough to handle, cut the very top and bottom off the squash, then cut in half with a large knife and remove the skin with a vegetable peeler. Scoop out the seeds and stringy bits with a spoon, then cut the flesh into 3 cm (1½ ") cubes.

Halve, peel and thinly slice the onion, garlic and the trimmed celery. Heat the oil in a large soup pan and gently cook the onion, garlic and grated ginger with a pinch of salt, covered, until soft and golden, about 8 minutes. Add the celery, squash and stock, then cover and simmer for 20 minutes or until the vegetables are soft when pierced with a sharp knife.

Peel 3 strips of zest from the orange, avoiding the bitter white pith, add the zest to the soup, then purée in a blender or food processor until absolutely smooth. Return to the pan and stir in the juice of the orange, the lime juice and seasonings.

To make the frizzled ginger, peel and slice the ginger as thinly as you can. Stack up the slices then cut them into very thin shreds. Heat the oil in a very small saucepan or frying pan, add the ginger (it should sizzle) and stir fry for 1-2 minutes until golden. Remove with a slotted spoon and drain on paper towels.

To serve, bring the soup to a simmer then garnish each bowl with a little pile of frizzled ginger, or serve with Whole Grain Croutons (page 43) or Greek yoghurt.

JUDI'S TIP: if the soup was frozen and tastes a bit muted after reheating, ½ teaspoon of freshly grated ginger and 5 grinds of black pepper will soon perk up its flavour.

CARROT & APPLE SOUP

Serves: 6
Keeps: 3 days in the fridge
Freeze: 3 months
Per serving: 130 cals, 19 g carbs

A lovely soup with bright zingy flavours, rich in vitamins A and C that support the immune system. Whole grain croutons with a hint of garlic add a contrasting crunch. Make the soup a day or two ahead for the full flavour to develop. The croutons can also be made ahead and frozen until needed.

---

1 medium onion

2 cloves garlic

300 g (10 oz) carrots

2 Braeburn or Cox's apples

2 tbsp olive oil

400 g tin of chopped tomatoes

½ tsp fresh or dried thyme, or dried mixed herbs

1 bay leaf

1.5 litres (2 ½ pints) strong vegetable stock

½-1 tsp fine sea salt

10 grinds black pepper

For the croutons

3 medium slices multiseed or whole grain bread

2 cloves garlic

2 tbsp olive oil

pinch fine sea salt

Peel and thinly slice the onion, garlic, and carrots. Peel, core and roughly chop the apples. Heat the oil in a large heavy-based soup pan. Gently sauté the onion and garlic with a pinch of salt, covered, over gentle heat, stirring occasionally, until very soft and golden, about 10 minutes. Add the carrots, cook for a few minutes longer, then add all the remaining soup ingredients. Bring to the boil, cover, and simmer gently for 45 minutes.

Remove the bay leaf, purée the soup in a blender or food processor until smooth, then taste. It should have a bright flavour, with a balance of sweetness and tartness. If the apples or tomatoes used were rather acidic and the soup tastes too sharp, add a pinch of cane sugar or erythritol to balance the flavour.

To make the croutons, preheat the oven to 200°C/Gas 6. Stack the slices of bread in a pile then cut into 1 cm (½") cubes with a bread knife. Smash the unpeeled garlic cloves with the side of a knife to release their flavour but leave the skin on.

Spread the cubes of bread and garlic on a non-stick baking tray, drizzle with the oil and salt, then toss with your fingers or a large spoon to coat thoroughly. Bake for 15-20 minutes, shaking the tin halfway through, until crisp and golden brown then discard the garlic and transfer to a bowl, or freeze in a sealed bag until needed.

Reheat the soup until bubbling and serve with the croutons.

FLORENTINE CHICKPEA & SPINACH SOUP

Serves: 4-6
Keeps: 1 week in the fridge
Freeze: 3 months
Per serving: 144 cals, 14 g carbs

A creamy soup, fragrant with rosemary and the nutty flavour of chickpeas that comes together in less than 15 minutes.

Nutritionally this soup has it all — rosemary to fight inflammation, garlic for heart health and protection against infection, fibre to lower cholesterol and blood sugar, olive oil for healthy monounsaturated fat and antioxidants, and last but not least, a handful of spinach to bump up the iron and vitamin content.

2 × 400 g tins chickpeas

3 cloves garlic

2 tbsp extra virgin olive oil

1 tsp finely chopped
   fresh rosemary,
   or ½ tsp dried rosemary

pinch chilli flakes

1 tbsp tomato purée
   or sun-dried tomato purée

½ litre (17 fl oz) strong
   vegetable stock

120-150 g baby spinach

½ tsp salt

10 grinds black pepper

extra virgin olive oil
   or chilli oil to serve

Rinse and drain the chickpeas, reserving a couple of tablespoons for garnishing the finished soup.

In a soup pan, gently heat the garlic, peeled and crushed in a press, with the oil and rosemary for 2-3 minutes until fragrant. Add the chilli flakes, tomato purée, chickpeas, and stock.

Simmer for 5 minutes, then purée the mixture until smooth, either in the pan with a stick blender, or in a blender or food processor. Bring the soup back to a simmer, add the spinach and seasonings then bubble, uncovered, for 2-3 minutes until the spinach is wilted but still bright green.

Top each serving with a few chickpeas and a drizzle of extra virgin olive or chilli oil. The soup may thicken on standing. If still very thick after reheating, thin it down slightly with a little hot stock or water.

SPINACH AND ROCKET, like many dark leafy greens, are loaded with phytonutrients vitamin A for immunity, night vision, cataract prevention and heart health, B vitamins for brain health, vitamin C which helps reduce infections, vitamin E for heart health, and vitamin K for blood clotting and bone strength.

CHICKEN BONE BROTH OR STOCK

Makes: about 1.75 litres (3 pints)
Keeps: 3 days in the fridge
Freeze: 3 months
Per serving: 20 cals, 5 g carbs

Next time you roast a chicken, freeze the cooked carcass and you'll have the foundation for Chicken Soup (page 48) and a host of other recipes. Roasting the bones — a classic French technique — adds tons of flavour, renders most of the fat, and removes the need for skimming any scum off the broth as it cooks.

It's also a great way to use up those jaded vegetables or scraps you might otherwise throw away – carrot peelings, celery roots, leek tops, onion skins, squashy tomatoes. We keep a bag in the freezer and stockpile them for just this purpose.

Emerging research suggests that bone broth may help to protect the intestinal barrier between the body and the gut, which could be helpful for sufferers of Crohn's disease, IBS, and colitis. Either way, it provides a wealth of vitamins and minerals including vitamin K2, calcium and phosphorous for healthy bones, and collagen which may benefit your hair, skin, nails and joints.

2-3 roast chicken carcasses, or 900 g (2 lb) uncooked parts (wings, thighs, necks, or backbones)

1 large onion

2 large carrots

½ small head celery

green part of a fat leek

2 squishy tomatoes

¼ tsp turmeric

handful of parsley

1.75 litres (3 pints) water

1 tsp salt

1 tsp black peppercorns

2 chicken stock cubes

If using roast chicken carcasses, cut them up with a strong pair of kitchen shears so they will fit in a stockpot or large soup pan. If using uncooked joints and giblets, preheat the oven to 200°C/Gas 6. Arrange them on a foil-lined baking tray and roast for 25-30 minutes.

Slice the washed but unpeeled vegetables thickly then add to the pot with the chicken and all the remaining ingredients. Cover and simmer very gently for 3 hours, either on top of the stove or in the oven at 150°C/Gas 2 where it will develop an even richer flavour.

When cool, strain the liquid into a second pan or bowl, discarding the vegetables and bones, which by now will have given their all to the stock. Add the crumbled stock cubes and simmer for 5 minutes. It can now be enjoyed as a light, clear broth, or frozen or chilled.

JUDI'S TIP: freeze some of the stock in ice cube trays or small containers to use when just a small amount is needed in sauces or stir fries.

CHICKEN SOUP & MATZAH BALLS

Serves: 4-6
Keeps: 3 days in the fridge
Freeze: 3 months
Per serving:
Soup 22 cals, 5 g carbs
Matzah balls 125 cals, 9 g carbs

Chicken Soup, aka Jewish penicillin, is one of the world's great comfort foods. And now scientists have confirmed what Jewish grandmothers have known for centuries – it's good for you!

As a young wife making chicken soup and matzah balls (knaidlach) for her new husband Myer, Evelyn Rose discovered the hard way that one family's perfect knaidlach are another one's cannonballs! If your family like them very soft, add an extra tablespoon each of oil and soup to the mixture.

Using chicken bone broth adds a wonderful depth of flavour to the soup. We've also added some healthy twists to the matzah balls. Oat bran, undetectable in the finished matzah balls, helps lower cholesterol, and ground almonds are a good source of vitamin E, which protects against UV light damage and Alzheimer's. Almonds also contain monounsaturated fat that can reduce the risk of heart disease (if you're allergic to nuts, use an extra 2 tablespoons of oat bran instead). Last but not least, we've replaced the traditional schmaltz (chicken fat) or margarine with heart-healthy olive oil.

For the soup

1.75 litres (3 pints)
   Chicken Bone Broth (page 47)
3 young carrots
white part of a leek
1-2 sticks celery
5 grinds white or black pepper

For the matzah balls

2 large eggs
100 g (3 ½ oz) medium
   or fine matzah meal
30 g (1 oz) ground almonds
1 tbsp oat bran
pinch ground ginger
½ tsp fine sea salt
90 ml (6 tbsp) tepid
   chicken soup
pinch of white pepper
60 ml (4 tbsp) olive oil

To make the soup, thinly slice or finely dice the trimmed and peeled carrots, leek, and celery. Put all the ingredients into a large soup pan and simmer until the vegetables are tender, 10- 15 minutes.

To make the matzah balls, whisk the eggs in a bowl with a rotary whisk or electric hand mixer for 2 minutes until light and frothy. Add all the remaining ingredients and mix gently with a fork until evenly blended. Your mixture should be moist and thick but not quite firm enough to form into balls. Pop it into the fridge, covered with clingfilm for half an hour or so to firm up.

Half-fill a large soup pan with water and bring to a simmer. Take pieces of the chilled mixture the size of a large walnut and roll into balls. If you first wet your palms very slightly, you'll find you can make smoother, rounder balls. Drop the balls into the simmering water, then cover and simmer for 30-40 minutes without removing the lid. Transfer them to the simmering chicken soup with a slotted spoon and serve.

JUDI'S TIP: to make the matzah balls ahead, cook then freeze them on a baking paper-lined tray until solid, then store in a sealed freezer bag. They can be reheated from frozen in the simmering soup.

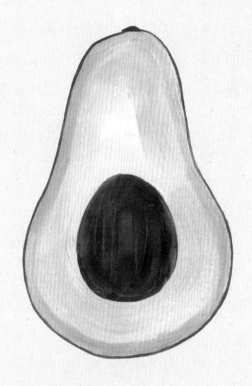

2 | LIGHT BITES

MELON & AVOCADO SALAD
WITH A GINGER VINAIGRETTE

Serves: 6-8
Keeps: melon and avocado
(separately) up to 12 hours
in the fridge
Per serving: 285 cals, 25 g carbs

Time to pull out the melon baller that's been sitting in your kitchen drawer for years. Melon is a great source of potassium and avocados are rich in vitamin E and heart-healthy monounsaturated fats. For a vegan version, simply omit the salmon.

For the ginger vinaigrette

2 tsp lemon juice
2 tbsp white wine vinegar
½ tsp mustard powder
2 tbsp olive oil
2 tbsp walnut oil
good pinch of sea salt
8 grinds of black pepper
generous pinch ground ginger

For the salad

3 large ripe avocados
1 ripe Galia, Ogen,
  or honeydew melon
½ small seedless watermelon
125 g (4 oz) Fennel or Beetroot
  Cured Salmon (page 122)
sprigs of basil, mint or dill

Put the lemon juice, vinegar and mustard into a screw-top jar and shake well. Add the rest of the vinaigrette ingredients and shake again to form a creamy emulsion.

Halve and pit the avocados, then use the smaller end of a melon baller to scoop out balls. If you don't have a melon baller, quarter then peel the pitted avocados and cut the flesh into 2.5cm (1") cubes. Submerge the avocado in the vinaigrette and chill for several hours.

Use the melon baller to scoop out the flesh from the halved and seeded melons, or remove the skin and cut the flesh into 2.5 cm (1") cubes. Place in a sieve over a bowl and chill. Roll up each slice of salmon into a long thin roll, cover with clingfilm, and chill.

Up to an hour before serving, add the melon to the avocado and mix gently. Cut each roll of salmon into tiny rolls, each about 2 cm (¾") long.

To serve, divide the melon and avocado and their dressing between 6 or 8 glasses or small dishes, add 3 rolls of salmon to each, and finish with sprigs or leaves of the herbs.

JUDI'S TIP: home-cured salmon is easy to make. Although much more expensive, you can also use bought smoked salmon. Avoid so-called "trimmings" or "cocktail pieces", however, which are fine for paté but neither look nor taste very nice in this dish.

RAINBOW SMOOTHIE BOWL

Serves: 3-4
Serve freshly made
Per serving: 227 cals, 30 g carbs

This bowl of healthy, energy-boosting deliciousness is a brilliant way to start the day. It's full of fibre and antioxidants that may help reduce the risk of cancer, Alzheimer's, heart disease, and stroke.

2 tbsp pomegranate juice

2 very ripe bananas

½ small ripe avocado

1 small cooked beetroot

100g (3 ½ oz) fresh
  or frozen strawberries

100 g fresh or frozen
  mixed berries

2 tbsp Greek yoghurt

squeeze of lemon juice

selection of seasonal fresh fruit

1-2 tbsp Supercrunch Granola

Peel and slice the banana then peel, pit and roughly chop the avocado and beetroot. Reserve some of the berries for the topping. Put the juice in a blender or food processor, add all the remaining ingredients except the granola and seasonal fruit, then purée until smooth. Chill, covered, for up to 30 minutes.

Shortly before serving, peel, trim, pit or slice the seasonal fruit – berries, peaches, plums, and bananas are some of our favourites.

Transfer the smoothie mixture to a shallow bowl or divide it between 3 or 4 glasses and arrange the fruit and granola on top, as artistically or otherwise as you like. Serve and enjoy.

SUPERCRUNCH GRANOLA

Serves: 10-12
Keeps: 1 month
in an airtight jar or container
Per serving: 190 cals, 27 g carbs

Our crunchy clusters of oats, nuts and seeds, studded with succulent dried fruit, have a fraction of the sugar of most commercial granola. Egg white adds protein and crunch but can be omitted for a vegan version, or omit the honey and egg and enjoy it raw as muesli.

25 g (1 oz) walnuts, pecans,
  almonds or hazelnuts

2 tbsp sunflower seeds

1 tbsp pumpkin or flax seeds

250 g (9 oz) gluten-free rolled oats

¼ tsp grated nutmeg

1 tsp ground cinnamon

pinch of salt

55 ml (2 fl oz) melted coconut
  or olive oil

60 g (2 oz) clear honey

85 g (3 oz) mixed dried fruit

1 large egg white

Preheat the oven to 150°C/Gas 2. Have ready a very large baking tray. Roughly chop the nuts then mix with the seeds, oats, spices and salt in a large bowl. Stir in the oil and honey, mixing thoroughly until blended.

Whisk the egg white by hand or electric whisk until it holds stiff peaks like meringue, then gently fold into the oat mixture with a rubber spatula. Spread the mixture over the baking tray and bake for 35-40 minutes or until a rich golden brown, rotating it halfway through so the granola browns evenly.

Remove from the oven and leave to cool on the baking sheet – as it cools it becomes crunchy. Chop dried fruit other than raisins or sultanas into bite-sized pieces and add to the granola.

JERUSALEM HUMMUS
WITH ZA'ATAR & PINE NUTS

Serves: 6-8 as a dip
Keeps: 5 days in the fridge
Freezes: 3 months
Per serving: 130 cals, 8 g carbs

Making your own hummus is simple and it freezes well too. For the best flavour, use freshly ground cumin and serve the hummus at room temperature.

Beans and chickpeas are packed with protein and fibre, while cumin is carminative so reduces any digestive side effects. Tahini paste, made from ground roasted sesame seeds, helps lower cholesterol. If someone is allergic to sesame, omit the tahini and za'atar and use only 1 tablespoon of water.

CANNELLINI

400 g tin ~~tinnellini~~ beans
    or chickpeas
1 clove garlic
juice of a lemon, about 3 tbsp
4 rounded tbsp tahini paste
2-4 tbsp water
2 tsp ground cumin
1 tsp ground coriander
½ tsp fine sea salt
15 grinds black pepper
1 ½ tbsp extra virgin olive oil

To serve
1 tsp za'atar (see page 11)
pinch of paprika or sumac
extra virgin olive oil
1 tbsp toasted pine nuts

Drain and rinse the beans or chickpeas. Peel and roughly chop the garlic. Put all the ingredients except the oil in a food processor or blender with 2 tablespoons of water and process until smooth, scraping down the sides of the bowl once or twice.

With the motor running, add the oil and process until smooth, light and creamy rather than thick and heavy. Add a little more water if necessary (the exact amount needed will depend on how thick your tahini paste was). Transfer the hummus to a container, cover, and leave for several hours. It will thicken and mellow as it matures.

To serve, spoon the hummus into a shallow bowl and smooth with the back of a teaspoon to create concentric circles. Sprinkle with the za'atar, paprika or sumac, drizzle with a dash of extra virgin olive oil, and top with the pine nuts. Serve with a basket of pita, warm Za'atar Flatbread (page 66) or Crispy Pita Triangles (page 67).

JUDI'S TIPS: some recipes use the liquid from the canned beans or chickpeas rather than water to thin the hummus, however this liquid often contains starch, preservatives, lots of salt, and compounds that can make the chickpeas harder to digest. Hence my preference for water. In Israel, some cooks swear by crushed ice cubes! If you prefer to start with dried pulses and cook them yourself, use 120 g (4 oz) which, after cooking, will yield about the same as a 400 g tin.

SMOKY AUBERGINE DIP

Serves: 6 as a dip
Keeps: 5 days in the fridge
Freezes: 3 months
Per serving: 115 cals, 10 g carbs

Chatzilim, or potlajel, is a much-loved Romanian-Israeli salad made of charcoal-grilled aubergines, lemon, garlic and herbs. This version is popular throughout the Levant, where it's known variously as moutabel, salat chatzilim, or baba ganoush. It includes tahini but can be made without it if someone is allergic to sesame.

The secret to a great smoky flavour is letting the skin of the aubergines blacken, most easily done on a barbecue, but oven-grilling works too. For an extra smoky flavour, hold the cooked aubergine over a gas flame with a pair of metal tongs, or use a kitchen blow torch to lightly char the skin.

---

675 g (1½ lb) glossy aubergines
3 sprigs flat leaf parsley
2 medium cloves garlic
4 tbsp lemon juice
4 tbsp tahini paste
2 tsp ground cumin
½ tsp ground coriander
½ tsp fine sea salt
15 grinds black pepper

To serve
1 tsp chopped parsley
1 tbsp pomegranate seeds
extra virgin olive oil

Preheat the oven to 230°C/Gas 8 (fan grill if possible). Line a baking tray with foil.

Cut the prickly stems off the aubergines, then prick all over with a fork to stop them bursting as they cook. Place the aubergines directly on the oven rack with the foil lined baking tray on the rack below to catch the drips. Cook for 25-30 minutes, turning once or twice, until the aubergines have begun to collapse and feel absolutely tender when pierced with a skewer.

Meanwhile, discard the coarse stalks from the parsley and put in a food processor with the peeled, thinly sliced garlic. Process until finely chopped.

When cool enough to handle, scoop the flesh out of the aubergines and add to the food processor (don't worry if some of the skin is attached). Add the lemon juice, tahini, spices and seasonings then pulse until you have a creamy but slightly textured purée. Serve at room temperature in a shallow bowl, sprinkled with parsley, pomegranate seeds, and a drizzle of olive oil.

AUBERGINES help protect the brain and spinal cord, and may help to reduce your risk of dementia. They're also high in fibre. Like rhubarb and spinach, they are high in oxalate, a naturally occurring chemical best avoided by those who are prone to calcium oxalate kidney stones.

KATSIS KISHUIM ISRAELI COURGETTE PATE

Serves: 8
Keeps: 3 days in the fridge
Do not freeze
Per serving: 90 cals, 3 g carbs

A delicious alternative to traditional chopped liver. The secret is to bring out the wonderful "umami" flavour of the vegetables by caramelising them until they're a rich, deep brown, the onions by patient braising, the courgettes by quick sautéing.

1 medium onion
1 tbsp olive oil
2 medium courgettes
1-2 tbsp coconut or rapeseed oil
½ tbsp butter
½ tsp fine sea salt
10 grinds of black pepper
pinch of cayenne or paprika
large sprig of parsley
2 hard-boiled eggs

To serve
sumac or paprika
sea salt flakes

Peel and thinly slice the onion. Heat a tablespoon of the oil in a heavy non-stick sauté pan, add the onion and a pinch of salt, then cook gently, covered, until very soft and golden, about 10 minutes. Uncover and cook for another 8-10 minutes, stirring from time to time, until the onions are a rich golden brown but still soft.

While the onions are cooking, trim and slice the courgettes as thinly as possible. Heat a tablespoon of the coconut or rapeseed oil in a wok or very large frying pan. When very hot, add half the courgettes, spread them out in a thin layer, and sprinkle with a pinch of salt.

Sauté over high heat until a rich brown on both sides, 4-6 minutes, then transfer to a plate. Stir fry the rest of the courgettes, adding more oil if needed. Add the courgettes, butter and seasonings to the onions.

Discard the coarse stalks and roughly chop the parsley, then pulse in a food processor until finely chopped. Add the eggs and the vegetables and pulse until the mixture is the texture of chopped liver. Taste the paté – it should be highly seasoned. If not, add a dash more salt, pepper and paprika.

Turn into a small bowl and leave to cool. Or chill until needed but let it come to room temperature for at least half an hour before serving. Just before serving, sprinkle with sumac or paprika and a few flakes of sea salt.

GEHAKTE HERRING CHOPPED HERRING SALAD

Serves: 8 spread on challah, crackers or rye bread
Keeps: 2 days in the fridge.
Do not freeze
Per serving: 180 cals, 15 g carbs

For the aristocracy of Czarist Russia, salt herring in its many forms was an essential part of the "zakuski" table, whose tasty titbits were considered ideal partners for a glass (or three) of vodka. For the poor Jews of the Pale of Settlement, herring was a cheap and nourishing form of protein – give the menfolk a couple of herrings a day and expensive meat could be saved for a Sabbath treat.

The traditional recipe for gehakte, or chopped, herring uses sweet digestive biscuits and a hefty six teaspoons of sugar to counteract the sourness of cooking apples and acetic acid. By using fruitier, gentler apple cider vinegar, and sweet yet tangy eating apples, just a teaspoon of sugar is all that's needed for a lovely balance of sweet and sour.

---

6 large free range eggs
6 rollmops (pickled herrings)
1 very small red onion
2 medium Braeburn or similar
   sweet but tart eating apples
2 tbsp ground almonds
1 tsp cider vinegar
1 tsp caster sugar,
   or ½ tsp erythritol
pinch of white pepper
pinch of sea salt

To serve
tiny sprigs of dill
a slice of lemon, quartered

Boil the eggs for 8 minutes, then pour off the water and run under the cold tap until cool, before shelling and halving them. Reserve one half for the garnish.

Drain the rollmops and pat dry on paper towels, then cut them into chunks and remove the skin where possible. Peel and roughly chop the onion, pulse in the food processor until finely chopped, then transfer to a mixing bowl. Process the unpeeled, cored, and quartered apples in the same way, then add them to the onion.

Put the herring, ground almonds and eggs (except the reserved half) into the food processor with the vinegar, sugar and seasonings. Process until finely chopped. Return the chopped apple and onion to the food processor, pulse briefly to blend, then taste and re-season if needed.

Pile the mixture into a dish, cover and chill. Just before serving, grate the reserved egg on top, garnish with the dill and lemon, and serve with rye bread, whole grain crackers or challah.

OILY FISH like herring, mackerel and salmon, are rich in omega-3 that is great for the brain and may help reduce the risk of cancer.

KIBBUTZ STYLE CHOPPED EGG & ONION

Serves: 8 as a starter
12 as spread or dip
Keeps: 2 days in the fridge
Do not freeze
Per serving: 253 cals, 9 g carbs

An Israeli twist on an Ashkenazi Friday night classic. Instead of the traditional schmaltz (chicken fat) or margarine, we use rich and creamy avocados. Like chopped liver and chopped herring, it was traditionally made with a hackmesser and hackbrettle, a wooden-handled chopper and cutting board (I still have my grandmother's) but nowadays a few pulses in the food processor does the job in seconds. Eggs are a good source of protein, choline, and folate for heart and brain health.

---

4 large free-range eggs
small bunch of parsley
small bunch of spring onions
4 ripe avocados
1 tbsp lemon juice
1 tsp sea salt
10 grinds black pepper
1 tbsp Easy Lemon Mayonnaise
   (page 76) or shop-bought mayo

Hard boil the eggs, run them under cold water to cool, then shell and cut them in quarters.

To make with a food processor, roughly chop the trimmed parsley and spring onions then add to the food processor and pulse until evenly mixed. Peel, pit, and roughly chop the avocados and add to the food processor with the lemon juice, eggs and seasonings. Pulse just until the eggs are chopped but the mixture still has plenty of texture. Turn into a bowl and add just enough mayonnaise to bind the mixture into a rough paté.

Alternatively to make the traditional way, chop the parsley, eggs and spring onions with a large knife. Chop the pitted and peeled avocados, sprinkle with lemon juice then mash with a fork to a paste. Mix all the ingredients in a bowl into a coarse but creamy paté. Taste and re-season with extra salt and pepper if necessary, then chill until needed. Serve with whole grain challah or crackers.

AVOCADOS are rich in heart-healthy monounsaturated fat and vitamin E, which is protective against Alzheimer's disease. They're also a good source of potassium, which helps regulate blood pressure.

APPLE & PICKLED HERRING SALAD
WITH A CREAMY DILL DRESSING

Serves: 6-8
Keeps: 2 days in the fridge
Do not freeze
Per serving: Salad: 240 cals, 21 g
carbs, dressing 48 cals, 2 g carbs

Sour, sweet or salty, creamy, crispy or crunchy – apples seem to complement almost any taste and texture. Their crisp, tart flavour is a perfect foil for pickled herrings (rollmops) in a creamy sweet and sour dressing.

This pretty salad - an old family recipe - is but one of a whole genre of Ashkenazi salads made with herring, fruit and vegetables - even nuts - bound with a sour cream sauce. It's quite mild in flavour when tasted a few hours after preparation, but after a day or so it takes on a pleasing piquancy.

Herring is a good source of omega-3 and vitamin D for a healthy heart and brain. For a vegetarian version, use 125 g (4 oz) seedless grapes instead.

450 g jar rollmops
  (pickled herrings)
2 Braeburn or similar crisp,
  flavourful eating apples
4 stalks celery
50 g (2 oz) sultanas, goji
  berries or dried cranberries

Dry the rollmops on paper towels then cut them into 3 cm (1") diagonal pieces. Core and quarter the unpeeled apples and cut them into 1 cm (½") cubes. Cut the trimmed celery into ½ cm (¼") slices.

Put the herring, apple, celery, and dried fruit in a bowl. Mix the dressing ingredients together, pour over the herring and apple mixture and mix gently. Refrigerate for several hours.

Just before serving, transfer to a serving dish and sprinkle with the roughly chopped nuts and tiny sprigs of dill.

For the dressing
1 tbsp chopped fresh dill
275 ml (10 oz) lower fat
  soured cream
1 tsp white wine vinegar
½ tsp Dijon mustard

To serve
50 g (2 oz) toasted pecans
  or walnuts
sprigs of dill

APPLES contain a remarkable antioxidant called quercetin that may lower blood pressure and reduce the risk of diabetes, heart disease, and asthma. They're also high in pectin, a soluble fibre that's great for digestive health, and vitamin C that helps the body absorb iron, boosts immunity, and improves wound healing.

ZA'ATAR FLATBREADS

Serves: 6-8
Keeps: 3 days in the fridge
Freeze: 3 months
Per serving: 150 cals, 24 g carbs

These magically puff up in the oven and form a pocket that's perfect for filling with falafel or salad. They're at their most delicious freshly baked, but you can make the dough ahead and bake the breads just before serving. Using some wholemeal flour adds fibre and reduces the glycaemic index. Za'atar is anti-inflammatory and antioxidant but use nigella seeds instead if someone is allergic to sesame.

4 level tbsp Greek yoghurt

200 ml (7 fl oz) warm (not hot) water

1 tbsp olive oil

115 g (4 oz) wholemeal bread flour

170 g (6 oz) very strong white bread flour (Canadian is best)

11 g sachet or 2½ tsp instant (easy blend) yeast

1 tsp caster sugar or erythritol

1 tsp fine sea salt

For the topping

1-2 tbsp za'atar, sesame or nigella seeds (see page 11) or some of each

sea salt

Put the yoghurt, water and oil into the bowl of a food processor, or a stand mixer fitted with a dough hook. Add the flour, yeast, sugar and salt, then process or mix until a ball of dough is formed that leaves the side of the bowl clean. Continue to mix or process the dough for a further minute, then turn it onto a lightly floured work surface and knead vigorously by hand until it feels smooth and springy, about 5 minutes, working in a bit more flour if sticky. Place the dough in a deep bowl, cover with clingfilm or a large bag, and leave to rise until doubled in volume, 30-60 minutes depending on the temperature of your kitchen, or overnight in the fridge.

Half an hour before baking, put a pizza stone or baking sheet on the top rack of a cold oven and set it to 260°C/Gas 10 to preheat. Turn the risen dough out onto a lightly floured surface and knead gently. Divide into 8 equal pieces and form into balls. Flatten them slightly, then roll or stretch each ball into a 10 cm (4") circle. If your dough springs back, leave it to rest for 5 minutes then try again. Cover with a cloth and leave for 10 minutes.

Roll each circle into a 15 cm (6") oval. Sprinkle both sides with flour, then gently pull and stretch each circle into a 17 cm (7") oval. Brush lightly with water, sprinkle with za'atar or seeds and a little salt, then use your rolling pin to press the topping lightly into the dough. Using a well-floured pizza paddle or upside down baking tray, carefully slide as many flatbreads into the oven as will fit on the pizza stone or baking sheet. Bake for 3-5 minutes until puffy and pale gold. Remove from the oven and cover with a cloth to keep them warm and soft. Once the oven returns to 260°C/Gas 10, bake the rest. Serve warm.

JUDI'S TIPS: flour varies by brand, age and even the weather so use the given quantities as a guide only. If your dough isn't coalescing into a ball, add water, 1 teaspoon at a time, until it does. Or if it sticks to the spindle or dough hook, add more flour, a pinch at a time, until it rotates freely and leaves the sides of the bowl clean.

> Pictured overleaf

DUKKAH

Makes about 150 g (5 oz)
Keeps: 2 weeks
in an airtight container
Per tbsp: 36 cals, 2 g carbs

Dukkah, which means "to crush or pound" in Egyptian Arabic, is an irresistible, crunchy mix of toasted nuts, seeds and spices. It's usually made with hazelnuts, but we think the sweetness of cashew nuts contrasts beautifully with the citrusy tang of sumac. Cashews are high in heart-protective monounsaturated fats, calcium and fibre, seeds contain a host of minerals, healthy fats, and vitamin E, and sumac is high in antioxidants and vitamin C. Leave out the sesame seeds if someone has a sesame allergy.

100 g (3½ oz) raw cashew nuts
2 tbsp sesame seeds
1 tbsp cumin seeds
1 tbsp coriander seeds
1 tsp nigella seeds
1 tsp fennel seeds
2 tsp sumac
½ tsp fine sea salt

Preheat the oven to 180°C/Gas 4. Spread the nuts and seeds on a baking tray and roast for 5-8 minutes until the nuts are golden and the spices smell toasty. Leave to cool. Pulse the mixture in a food processor, or pound with a mortar and pestle, until the texture of fine gravel, then stir in the sumac and salt. Serve in a small dish or bowl with good bread and olive oil for dipping, or sprinkle over salads or dips.

CRISPY PITA TRIANGLES

Serves: 6-8
Keeps: 1 week
in an airtight container
Freeze: 1 month
Per pita: 215 cals, 33 g carbs

These little herby nibbles are brilliant served with dips, or on their own as a snack. Za'atar, which contains sesame seeds, has antioxidant properties, is anti-inflammatory, and can help control cholesterol, but leave it out if someone is allergic to sesame.

6 wholemeal pitas or flatbreads
2 tbsp extra virgin olive oil
2 tsp za'atar
½ tsp fine sea salt

Preheat the oven to 200°C/Gas 6. Stack three of the pitas on top of one another and cut them into 6-8 triangles with scissors or kitchen shears so you have 18-24 pieces. Repeat with the other three pitas.

Mix the oil, salt, and za'atar in a large bowl. Add the triangles, toss to coat, then spread them on a large baking tray. Bake for 15-20 minutes or until crisp and golden, shaking the tray and turning them over halfway through. Serve warm, or store in an airtight container once cool. May be reheated at 180°C/Gas 5 for 5-8 minutes.

> Pictured overleaf

SESAME CRUSTED FALAFEL

Serves: 6-8
Keeps: 2 days in the fridge
Freeze: 2 months
Per serving: 265 cals, 32 g carbs

Making falafel from scratch isn't hard and so much tastier than using a mix. Oven-baking them with a little oil– a technique known as air-frying – instead of the usual deep fat frying, makes these crunchy morsels far healthier but no less delicious.

We like to set up a self-serve falafel bar with the salads, pickles, condiments and a basket of warm pita or flatbread (page 66). Don't be tempted to use tinned chickpeas or your falafel may fall to bits. And if someone's allergic to sesame, omit the seeds in the coating, and serve without tahina sauce or za'atar flatbread.

300 g (10 oz) dried chickpeas
¼ of a medium onion
4 cloves garlic
a good handful of parsley
½ tsp salt
1 tsp cumin seeds
   or ground cumin
1 tbsp lemon juice
pinch of cayenne or chilli powder
1-2 tbsp water

For the sesame coating
3-4 tbsp sesame seeds
2 tbsp olive oil

To serve
½ long cucumber
8-10 cherry tomatoes
1 tsp extra virgin olive oil
¼ of a cabbage or lettuce
pickled hot peppers
Tahina Sauce (page 77)
2-3 tbsp harissa or similar
   chilli sauce
Za'atar Flatbread (page 66) or pita

Soak the chickpeas in plenty of water for at least 8 hours or overnight. Drain and rinse. Peel and roughly chop the onion and garlic. Put them into a food processor or blender with the rest of the ingredients and process until a thick paste is formed, scraping down the sides as needed. Transfer the mixture to a bowl and roll into 3 cm (1") balls, then flatten them slightly. The falafel can now be left for up to 2 hours before baking.

Up to an hour before serving, chop the cucumber and tomatoes and mix together with a pinch of salt and the extra virgin olive oil. Shred the cabbage or lettuce finely. Put the tomato and cucumber salad, shredded cabbage, pickles and the sauces into separate serving bowls and chill until needed.

Half an hour before serving, preheat the oven to 200°C/Gas 6. Pour the oil onto a non-stick baking tray. Add the falafel and jiggle the tray to coat them thoroughly with the oil, then sprinkle with the sesame seeds. Jiggle again until they are well coated with the seeds.

Bake the falafel for 15 minutes, then turn them over with a large spoon and bake for another 10-15 minutes until a rich brown on both sides – if not, place them under the grill for 2-4 minutes.

Meanwhile, heat the flatbreads or pitas in a toaster, then cut them in half to reveal the pocket. Serve at once with the falafel, salads and condiments.

CHICKPEAS help lower LDL cholesterol and reduce the risk of diabetes and bowel cancer. They're high in protein and fibre, and a good source of molybdenum, a mineral with antioxidant properties that's essential for a healthy metabolism.

QUICK CUCUMBER PICKLES

Serves: 6-8
Keeps: 1 week in the fridge
Per serving: 6 cals, 1 g carbs

Gently sweet and sour, this healthier rendering of a classic recipe takes moments to make. It can be eaten right away, but tastes even better after a few days in the fridge. Cucumber contains silica, which is good for hair, skin and nails. Vinegar helps regulate blood sugar and settle the digestion.

1 long or 3 short cucumbers

1 tbsp snipped dill or tarragon

1 tbsp hot water

3 tbsp rice vinegar or
  cider vinegar

5 grinds black pepper

1 tsp caster sugar or erythritol

Slice the unpeeled cucumber as thinly as possible, most easily done on a food processor using the slicing attachment, or with a mandoline slicer. Cut the slices into quarters and transfer to a bowl.

Mix the rest of ingredients together, pour over the cucumbers, then transfer to a jar or airtight container and chill until needed.

CRUNCHY SPICED CHICKPEAS

Serves: 4-6
Keeps: 3 days, but are best served freshly roasted
Per serving: 158 cals, 24 g carbs

These beat crisps and other "nosh" hands down. Feel free to use a tablespoon of your favourite spice mix – we like harissa spice. If you have time, dried chickpeas, soaked for several hours then boiled until tender turn out crunchier than their canned cousins. Like nuts, roasted chickpeas, are not suitable for infants due to the risk of choking.

125 g (4 oz) dried chickpeas, soaked and cooked, or a 400g tin chickpeas

generous tbsp olive oil

generous ½ tsp fine sea salt

1 tsp ground cumin

1 tsp paprika or smoked paprika

½ tsp cayenne or hot paprika

Preheat the oven to 200°C fan or 220°/Gas 7 conventional. Spread the drained chickpeas on a roasting tin or baking tray and place in the oven for 10 minutes to dry as it preheats. Add the oil and toss thoroughly until the chickpeas are well coated (I use two metal spoons to do this).

Roast for 10 minutes, give the tin a good shake, and roast for another 10 minutes. Add the salt and spices, shake well to coat, then leave to cool for 10 minutes in the oven with the heat off (the chickpeas will crispen as they cool). Eat the same day, or store in an airtight container then re-crispen if necessary at 180°C for 5 minutes.

CHICKEN LIVER PATE
WITH TARRAGON & PEARS

Serves: 6-8 as a starter,
or 10-12 as a spread
Keeps: 3 days in the fridge
(without leaves)
Per serving:
paté 183 cals, 12 g carbs
salad 115 cals, 17 g carbs

Crisp leaves, and sweet, succulent pears marinated in a tarragon and nut oil dressing transform a rustic paté into a sophisticated starter. Sometimes we sprinkle a tablespoon of pomegranate seeds or toasted pine nuts over the salad, or just serve the paté itself on crackers or whole grain challah. By replacing the schmaltz (chicken fat) or margarine used in traditional "gehakte leber" (chopped liver) with heart-healthy olive oil, and caramelising the onions, we've reduced the saturated fat without sacrificing flavour. Chicken liver itself is a nutritional powerhouse, rich in iron, and surprisingly low in saturated fat.

For the paté

1 Spanish onion

2-3 cloves of garlic

2 tbsp olive oil

3 large eggs

450 g (1lb) koshered
chicken livers

2 bay leaves

1 tsp fine sea salt

15 grinds black pepper

large pinch of ground nutmeg

2 tbsp extra virgin olive oil

tarragon leaves or chopped
pistachios to serve

For the salad

1 tbsp cider or white wine vinegar

2 tbsp olive oil

juice of ½ an orange or tangerine

3 tbsp hazelnut or walnut oil

2 tbsp finely chopped tarragon
leaves from 3-4 sprigs

½ tsp fine sea salt

15 grinds black pepper

4 ripe, juicy pears

180-200 g pack mixed leaf salad

Top and tail, halve, peel then thinly slice the onion and garlic. Fry them gently in the olive oil with a good pinch of salt in a large frying pan, covered, for 15-20 minutes until all the onion is very soft and a rich caramel brown. This is important to achieve the right depth of flavour, so be patient. Stir from time to time, reducing the heat if the onion starts to brown before it is soft. Meanwhile, hard boil the eggs for 10 minutes then drench with cold water, shell and cut in half.

Trim and quarter the livers, then add to the onions in the pan with the bay leaves and seasonings. Stir fry over brisk heat for a few minutes until the livers are a rich brown on the outside and opaque but still slightly pink in the centre (cut one in half to check).

Remove the bay leaves, then tip the contents of the pan into a food processor. Add the eggs and extra virgin olive oil, then process until you have a smooth, creamy paté with no visible egg white. Transfer to a container, cover and chill.

Put the vinegar, oils, juice, chopped tarragon and seasonings in a screw-top jar and shake well. Peel thick-skinned varieties of pear such as Conference if necessary, then halve them and remove the core, easiest with a small metal measuring spoon. If the pears are large, quarter or slice them thickly. Arrange in a shallow container, pour over the dressing, cover and chill.

Half an hour before serving, remove the paté from the fridge and divide it between 6-8 little ramekins, dishes or jars, topping each with some tarragon or chopped pistachios. Arrange the leaves on 6-8 salad plates, leaving room for the paté. Lift the pears from their dressing and divide between the plates, then add the dishes of paté. Just before serving, spoon the remaining dressing over the salad, or if you prefer, serve it separately for guests to add themselves.

SPINACH & HERB JIBN

Serves: 10-12 as a nibble,
4-6 as a light meal with salads
Keeps: 2 days in the fridge
Freeze: uncooked for 2 weeks
Per serving: 173 cals, 2 g carbs

1 bunch spring onions

pinch of salt

2 cloves garlic

40 g (1½ oz) butter

225 g (8 oz) baby spinach

6 large free range eggs

160 g pack garlic and herb
 soft cheese

10 grinds black pepper

1 level tbsp chopped parsley

175 g (4oz) grated
 extra mature cheddar

2 tbsp grated parmesan

To Persians they are kuku, to Egyptians eggah, and to Syrian cooks, who add cheese, they are jibn. Whatever the name, these creamy baked omelettes are one of the culinary glories of Sephardi cuisine.

Preheat the oven to 190°C/Gas 5. Lightly oil a 20 × 20 cm (8 × 8") ovenproof dish or cake tin and line the bottom and two of the sides with a strip of baking paper – this makes it much easier to remove the cooked jibn.

Thinly slice the trimmed spring onions, keeping the white and leafy green parts separate. Crush the peeled garlic with a press. Melt the butter in a large frying pan then add the spring onions, garlic and a pinch of salt. Cook gently until soft then add the spinach. Sauté over medium heat until the spinach is wilted and the liquid has evaporated.

Whisk the eggs in a medium bowl, then add the spinach, cheese, herbs and seasonings. Pour into the prepared dish, smooth the top with a spatula and bake for 30-40 minutes until golden brown and firm to the touch. Leave to cool slightly then turn out onto a cutting board. Using a large knife, cut the jibn into 40 bite-sized squares. Serve warm or at room temperature.

JUDI'S TIPS: to make things easy, I use a pack of ready-mixed soft cheese with garlic and herbs, but you can mix 160g (5 1/2 oz) reduced fat soft cheese with a clove of crushed garlic, a teaspoon each of snipped chives and Provençal herbs, 10 grinds of black pepper and a good pinch of sea salt. To serve as a main course for 4-6, cook the jibn in a 23 cm (9") oven proof non-stick frying pan or flan dish, and serve in wedges with a crisp green salad.

EASY LEMON MAYONNAISE

Serves: 8-10
Keeps: 2 weeks in the fridge
Do not freeze
Per serving: 233 cals, 1 g carbs

A tasty, lightly textured mayonnaise that's really quick and easy to make. Lemon juice and cayenne aid circulation, black pepper fights inflammation, and, like all fermented foods, vinegar is good for the digestion.

1 large egg
1 tsp Dijon mustard
1 tsp fine sea salt
5 grinds of black pepper
pinch of cayenne or hot paprika
1 tbsp fresh lemon juice
1 tsp caster sugar
   or erythritol
225 ml (8 fl oz) olive
   or rapeseed oil
50 ml (2 fl oz) extra virgin
   olive oil
1 tsp red or white wine vinegar

Put all the ingredients except the oil and vinegar into a food processor, blender, or tall beaker if using a hand-held blender. Process or blend for 15 seconds.

Put the oils into a measuring jug. With the motor running, starting very gradually with just a few drops at a time, pour a very thin stream of oil onto the egg mixture. It should gradually lighten in colour and become thick and creamy. Finally, add the vinegar and process until evenly mixed. Taste and reseason if necessary, then transfer to a jar or airtight container and store in the fridge.

GREEN HERB OR BEETROOT MAYONNAISE

For Green Herb Mayonnaise, make as for the lemon mayonnaise but add 1 tablespoon of snipped chives, a small handful of parsley (no stalks) and a small, peeled clove of garlic, crushed in a press, to the egg and seasonings.

For Beetroot Mayonnaise, omit the herbs and add a roughly chopped, cooked (not pickled) beetroot to the egg and seasonings. Proceed as before. Or for a chunkier version, gently stir chopped beetroot into the finished mayonnaise instead of processing it with the other ingredients.

JUDI'S TIPS: as a shortcut, make the Green Herb or Beetroot Mayonnaise using bottled mayo. Just mix your finely chopped herbs, pressed garlic, a squeeze of lemon juice and a few grinds of black pepper with 260 g (9 oz) of high quality – ideally organic – mayonnaise. Because bottled mayo does not contain raw egg, this is handy if serving pregnant women or others who may be particularly vulnerable to infection (see page 9). Eggs that carry a British red Lion stamp, however, are from hens vaccinated against salmonella, so considered safe for anyone to eat raw.

TWO MINUTE TAHINA SAUCE

Serves: 6-8
Keeps: 2 weeks in the fridge
Freeze: 2 months
Per serving: 51 cals, 1 g carbs

Brilliant with falafel or flatbread. If you plan to make it more than a couple of days ahead, don't add the parsley until a few hours before serving. Tahini paste is rich in vitamin E for a healthy heart, B vitamins for a healthy brain, and can help lower LDL cholesterol, but is not suitable for anyone with a sesame allergy.

3 tbsp tahini paste
  (see page 11)
3-4 tbsp water
juice of ½ a lemon
¼ tsp fine sea salt
5 grinds black pepper
1 tbsp chopped flat parsley

In a small bowl or mini food processor, mix all the ingredients with a small whisk or process until smooth. The mixture may thicken and seize up at first, but keep mixing until it is pale and creamy. If very thick and sticky, add an extra teaspoon of water or lemon juice until it is the consistency of pouring cream.

PICO DE GALLO FRESH TOMATO SALSA

Serves: 8-10
Eat same day
Per serving: 28 cals, 6 g carbs

Pico de gallo (pronounced peeko day guy-o) means "rooster's beak" although no one's sure how this refreshing salsa fresca, or fresh salsa, got its name. Relished throughout the American Southwest, and perfect with fajitas, pico de gallo is quite different from the supermarket salsa sold in jars, and more like a juicy version of chachumber, the Indian onion and tomato relish often served with poppadoms. Tomatoes help lower blood pressure and your risk of heart disease. Chillies flight inflammation.

10-12 flavourful cherry
  or baby plum tomatoes,
  or 2 ripe plum tomatoes
½ small red onion
1 red or green jalapeño
  or other smallish chilli
2 tbsp chopped coriander
  or parsley
juice of ½ a lime
¼ tsp fine sea salt

Cut the tomatoes into small cubes. Halve the onion, remove the skin, and cut into very thin slices, then into very small dice. Trim, seed and finely chop the jalapeño pepper (wash your hands afterwards).

Mix all the ingredients together and leave for 30 minutes and up to three hours for the flavours to blend. Serve cool or at room temperature.

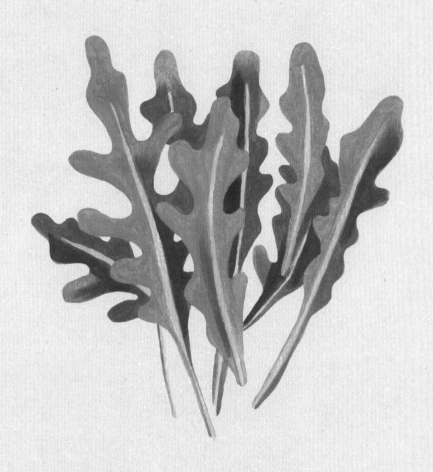

3 | SALADS

ORANGE & BEETROOT CARPACCIO

Serves: 6
Keeps: dressing 2 days
in the fridge
Eat carpaccio within 2 hours
Per serving: 123 cals, 17 g carbs

Carpaccio, named after an Italian Renaissance artist famous for his use of red and white tones, is traditionally made with paper-thin slices of meat or fish. Our magenta-hued vegan version, with its refreshing citrus dressing, makes a beautiful starter or side salad. For a really dramatic presentation, use some blood oranges and candy striped (chioggia) beetroots, which happily both happen to be in season around the same time.

For the orange vinaigrette

1 tbsp red wine vinegar
3 tbsp extra virgin olive oil
generous pinch of sea salt
5 grinds black pepper
1 small orange

For the salad

3 large oranges
2 cooked beetroots
1-2 young fresh beetroots
tiny sprigs of watercress,
   rocket, or pea shoots

To make the orange vinaigrette, put the vinegar, oil and seasonings into a screw-top jar. Zest and juice the small orange, add to the jar and shake well.

Cut a slice off the top and bottom of the large oranges then remove the peel and white pith with a small sharp knife. Slice the oranges thinly, adding any loose juice to your dressing.

Slice the cooked beetroot. Trim and peel the raw beetroot and slice as thinly as you can, ideally paper-thin and definitely no more than 2-3 mm (⅛″) thick, easiest using a mandoline or vegetable slicer.

Arrange the beetroot and orange slices on a serving platter then pour over half the vinaigrette. The carpaccio can now be refrigerated, covered with clingfilm, for up to 2 hours.

Just before serving, add the watercress, rocket, or pea shoots and drizzle with the rest of the well-shaken dressing.

BEETROOT, like most dark red and purple vegetables, is packed with anthocyanins, potent antioxidants that help combat cell damage. It's also brilliant for lowering blood pressure and helping circulation, good for detox, and may help reduce the risk of cancer.

CALIFORNIA WINTER SALAD
IN RED, GREEN & GOLD

Serves: 8-10
Keeps: 1 day in the fridge
Do not freeze
Per serving: 153 cals, 22 g carbs

This pretty salad, with its mix of tangy fruit, nuts and sweet peppers, goes well with salmon or cold chicken, or makes a refreshing chaser after a rich main course. High in vitamins A, C and folic acid – all good for heart and brain health – it sets you well on the way to your five-a-day.

For the salad

1 smallish pineapple
1 sweet red pointed pepper
1 small yellow pepper
2 large oranges
50 g (2 oz) walnuts
    or pecans
2 tbsp sultanas
200-300 g ready-to-eat
    mixed salad leaves

For the walnut vinaigrette

3 tbsp olive oil
1 tbsp walnut oil
3 tbsp lemon juice
½ tsp fine sea salt
10 grinds black pepper
¼ tsp paprika

Using a large sharp knife, cut the top and bottom off the pineapple, then remove the skin and any remaining "eyes". Now halve then quarter it lengthwise, remove the hard core from each section, and cut the flesh into 5 × 2.5 × 1 cm (2 × 1 × ½") pieces.

Trim the peppers and cut them into very thin slivers. Cut the peel and all the white pith off the oranges then use a small sharp knife to cut the flesh between the membrane into sections. Or, just slice the orange thinly and cut the slices into quarters if you find that easier.

Break the nuts into large pieces. Put them in an empty non-stick pan and toast by shaking them over gentle heat for 4 or 5 minutes, or until golden brown and slightly shiny. Make the walnut vinaigrette by putting all the ingredients in a screw-top jar and shaking well until an emulsion forms.

Up to an hour before serving, put the salad leaves, pineapple, peppers, oranges, sultanas and nuts into a serving bowl. Pour the dressing over the salad and toss lightly so everything is glistening and evenly coated. Chill until needed.

JUDI'S TIPS: for a creamy ranch-style dressing, add a tablespoon of Easy Lemon Mayonnaise (page 76) to the vinaigrette and shake well. If you're pushed for time, use ready-to-eat fresh pineapple chunks or fingers.

BABY AUBERGINE & ROASTED PEPPER SALAD

Serves: 6-8
Keeps: 2 days in the fridge
Do not freeze
Per serving: 184 cals, 15 g carbs

Layers of creamy aubergine and roasted pepper with a honey and garlic dressing. Use baby aubergines if possible, otherwise choose small, slender aubergines.

The key to delicious aubergines is to cook them until they've turned from firm and spongy to soft and meltingly tender, and the surface is a rich, caramel brown. Be patient.

Like all purple fruits, aubergines are good for brain health. Red peppers are rich in vitamin A for immunity and eye health, while pine nuts and pistachios help lower blood pressure.

---

1 kg (2 lb) baby aubergines
2-3 tbsp olive oil
fine sea salt
4 roasted red peppers,
   about half a jar

For the dressing

225 ml (8 fl oz) Greek yoghurt
1 large clove garlic
1 tsp ground cumin
2 tbsp finely chopped
   coriander or flat-leaf parsley
1 tbsp chopped fresh oregano
1 tsp thin honey
¼ tsp sea salt
15 grinds black pepper

To serve

50 g (2 oz) toasted pine nuts
1 tbsp pomegranate seeds
1 tbsp chopped flat-leaf parsley
extra virgin olive oil

Set the grill to high with the oven rack 8-10 cm (3-4″) below the element. Halve the baby aubergines lengthways, or cut regular sized ones into 1.5 cm (½″) diagonal slices. Arrange on a grill pan, brush generously with the oil on all sides, including the skin, and sprinkle both sides lightly with salt.

Grill for 10-15 minutes until golden brown on one side, then turn the slices over with a spatula and grill for another 10-15 minutes, until the second side is golden brown and the flesh is meltingly soft and creamy. Keep a close eye on the aubergines while grilling so they don't burn. Remove from the grill and cover lightly with foil.

To make the dressing, put the yoghurt in a bowl, add the garlic, peeled and crushed in a press, followed by the rest of the dressing ingredients, and whisk together with a fork until evenly mixed.

Drain the roasted peppers from their liquid and slice them thickly. Spread a quarter of the dressing in the centre of a large plate or shallow serving dish. Add a third of the aubergines, then a third of the peppers. Build up two more layers in the same way, ending with the remaining dressing.

Sprinkle with the pine nuts, pomegranate seeds and herbs, then finish with a generous drizzle of extra virgin olive oil. Serve at room temperature.

ROASTED SQUASH & PECAN SALAD

Serves: 6
Keeps: 2 days in the fridge
Do not freeze
Per serving: 305 cals, 17 g carbs

Roasting winter squash brings out its natural sweetness and nutty flavour, complemented here by crunchy pecans and an orange and walnut dressing. Butternut is the easiest squash to find, but if you can find them, more unusual varieties like Hubbard, Crown Prince and Musquée de Provence are more flavourful and nutritious. For a vegan version, add half a cup of cooked chickpeas or avocado cubes tossed with lime or lemon juice and a pinch of salt instead of the feta or goats' cheese.

50 g (2 oz) shelled pecans

1 large butternut squash

1 tbsp olive oil

½ tsp fine sea salt

10 grinds black pepper

200 -250 g pack mixed leaf salad, rocket or spinach

225 g (8 oz) crumbled feta or goats' cheese

For the dressing

1 tbsp freshly squeezed orange juice

1 tbsp lemon juice

2 tsp cider vinegar

3 tbsp olive oil

1 tbsp walnut or hazelnut oil

½ tsp sea salt

10 grinds black pepper

Set the oven to 225°C/Gas 7. Spread the pecans on a baking tray, and place in the oven to toast for 10 minutes as it heats up, or until golden brown. Remove the nuts but leave the oven on.

Soften the squash slightly in the microwave on high for 2-4 minutes, or in the oven for 5-10 minutes. When the squash is cool enough to handle, remove the skin with a vegetable peeler.

Cut the squash in half around its "waist" with a large, sharp knife, then scoop out the seeds and stringy bits with a spoon. Cut the flesh into 2.5 cm (1") thick slices and spread them on a non-stick baking tray. Sprinkle with the salt and pepper, drizzle with the oil, then toss them with your hands or a spoon until thoroughly coated.

Roast in the preheated oven for half an hour, then turn over the pieces using a spatula or tongs. Roast for another 10-15 minutes or until nicely browned on both sides.

To make the dressing, shake all the ingredients in a screw-top jar until an emulsion forms. Arrange the mixed leaves and squash in a serving dish, then sprinkle with the crumbled cheese and pecans. Just before serving, pour over the well-shaken dressing, and mix gently until everything glistens.

WINTER SQUASH is high in antioxidant carotenes, orange and yellow pigments that protect the health of your eyes and may lower the risk of cancer. The carotene content increases as squash ages and is boosted still further by roasting or steaming.

FRENCH BEANS WITH LEMON & TARRAGON

Serves: 6
Keeps: 2 days in the fridge
Do not freeze
Per serving: 59 cals, 6 g carbs

Evelyn and Myer Rose honeymooned in Biarritz, an adventurous, if not downright daring thing to do in the 1940s. It was the start of a lifelong love affair with France and its food.

Four decades later, they returned to the area to visit the legendary chef and restaurateur, Michel Guérard. A simple salad of lightly cooked haricots verts – freshly picked that morning from his "potager" – bathed in a lemony tarragon and chervil vinaigrette, was a mouthwatering reminder that even the humblest of dishes can be a feast when made with superb ingredients.

You can serve this salad either warm or at room temperature. To turn it into a main course, add some crumbled feta or goats' cheese and serve with toasted sourdough or whole grain bread.

---

225 g (8 oz) haricots verts
   or fine beans
225 g (8 oz) trimmed mangetout
   or sugar snap peas,
   or a mix of both
2 tbsp blanched almonds,
   pine nuts, or hazelnuts
1 lemon, unwaxed if possible

For the tarragon vinaigrette
1 tbsp extra-virgin olive oil
1 tbsp hazelnut or walnut oil
2 tbsp snipped fresh tarragon
½ tsp fine sea salt
15 grinds black pepper

Place a large colander in the sink. Bring a large pan of water to the boil then add a teaspoon of salt and the trimmed beans. Boil for 3 minutes, then add the mangetout or sugar snap peas and boil for 2-3 minutes or until bite-tender. Immediately tip the vegetables into the colander and drench with cold running water, mixing gently until all the vegetables feel cool. Tip them into a bowl of very cold water, leave for 3 minutes to set the colour, then drain.

Toast the nuts by shaking them in an empty frying pan over medium heat for 3-4 minutes until golden brown.

Pare 2 strips of zest from the lemon with a vegetable peeler, avoiding the bitter pith just under the fragrant yellow skin, then cut the peel into very thin slivers. Easier still, use a citrus zester, a bar tool with several tiny holes at the end. You'll need 1 or 2 teaspoons of slivered zest altogether. Set aside.

Put the oils, tarragon and seasonings into a screw-top jar. Juice half of the lemon then add the juice to the jar and shake well.

Transfer the vegetables to a salad bowl. Add the dressing and toss gently. Before serving, sprinkle with the nuts and shredded zest.

JUDI'S TIPS: the vegetables can be cooked the day before and chilled until needed. If you can't get haricots verts or fine beans, use regular green beans cut in half lengthwise, or string beans cut into diagonal pieces.

JEWELLED QUINOA

Serves: 4-6
Keeps: 1 week in the fridge
Freeze: 3 months
Per serving: 365 cals, 42 g carbs

Always ahead of her time, Evelyn Rose was already championing the culinary delights and health credentials of quinoa (pronounced "kin-wa") back in the early 1990s. An ancient grain from South America, quinoa has a nutty taste and a slightly chewy texture. The tiny spherical grains, which can be red, white or brown, are gluten-free and rich in protein, minerals, and fibre.

This colourful salad is laden with good stuff, from nuts and seeds to currants and kale, and can be served warm or at room temperature. As a short cut, use two 225g packs of ready to eat cooked quinoa, although it won't have quite the same texture or depth of flavour.

---

1 medium onion

1 orange or yellow pepper

½ bunch cavolo nero
  or curly kale

1 tbsp olive oil

250 g (9 oz) dried quinoa

1 orange

4 tbsp currants or raisins

1 tbsp goji berries
  or dried cranberries

500 ml (17 fl oz) vegetable stock

handful of broken cashew nuts

1 tbsp sunflower seeds

1 tbsp pumpkin seeds

For the dressing

2 tablespoons lemon juice

80 ml (3 fl oz) extra virgin olive oil

2 cloves garlic

1 tbsp low sodium light soy sauce

¼ tsp fine sea salt

10 grinds black pepper

Trim and finely chop the onion and pepper. Remove the stalks from the cavolo nero or kale, bunch up the leaves, slice thinly then chop into 3 cm (1½") pieces.

In a sauté pan or wide heavy-based saucepan, heat the oil then gently cook the onion with a pinch of salt, covered, for 8-10 minutes until soft and golden, stirring once or twice.

Peel 3 strips of zest from the orange with a vegetable peeler, avoiding the white pith, and reserve, then finely grate the rest. Add the grated zest, quinoa, currants or raisins and stock to the pan. Bring to the boil then simmer over low heat until the liquid has been absorbed and the quinoa is tender but not mushy, 10-15 minutes. Fluff up the grains with a fork, then mix in the red pepper, cavolo nero and berries.

To make the dressing, peel and crush the garlic in a press. Put the dressing ingredients, including the garlic, into a screw-top jar and shake well. Pour over the quinoa and mix gently. Check the seasoning, bearing in mind that the soy sauce and vegetable stock will have provided some salt, so it may only need pepper.

Shortly before serving, shred the reserved orange zest into very thin slivers. Scatter the nuts, seeds and zest over the salad and serve.

PINEAPPLE RICE WITH SESAME & CASHEWS

Serves: 6-8
Keeps: 2 days in the fridge
Do not freeze
Per serving: 215 cals, 30 g carbs

A cool, fresh take on pineapple fried rice, a south-east Asian favourite. It makes great bowl food for a crowd. To turn it into a main dish, add stir-fried chicken, mushrooms or extra firm tofu. Brown rice is a wonderful source of B vitamins, folic acid, and minerals. Omit the sesame seeds and sesame oil if someone has a sesame allergy.

175 g (6 oz) brown rice
½ tsp salt
50 g (2oz) cashew nuts
4 tbsp sesame seeds
1 small pineapple
1 sweet pointed red pepper
6 spring onions
50 g (2oz) currants or sultanas

For the dressing
1.5 cm (½") piece of fresh ginger
1 small fresh red chilli pepper
1 large clove garlic
2 tsp toasted sesame oil
2 tbsp extra virgin olive oil
4 tbsp reduced-salt soy sauce
2 tbsp lemon juice
good pinch of sea salt
8 grinds black pepper

Cook the rice with the salt according to package directions until bite-tender, typically 25 minutes for easy cook rice and 40 minutes for regular.

While the rice is cooking, make the dressing. Peel and finely grate the ginger and garlic, seed and finely chop the chilli, then add to a screw-top jar with the other dressing ingredients and shake well.

When the rice is cooked, drain if necessary, transfer to a bowl and add the dressing, mixing gently with a fork.

Spread the cashew nuts and sesame seeds at opposite ends of a baking tray. Set the oven to 180°C/Gas 4 and toast the nuts and seeds for 8-10 minutes while it heats up, shaking the tray halfway through. The nuts and seeds may brown at different rates, so watch them carefully and if necessary remove the seeds once golden so they don't burn.

Peel, quarter and core the pineapple then cut the flesh into small cubes. Trim, seed and finely chop the sweet pepper. Trim and thinly slice the white and green parts of the spring onions.

Add the remaining ingredients, except the nuts and seeds, mixing gently with a fork. Up to an hour before serving, sprinkle with the toasted nuts and seeds. Serve warm or at room temperature.

SESAME SEEDS help lower LDL cholesterol and may help prevent dementia. They're also rich in zinc, essential for a host of functions from wound healing and blood pressure to a normal sense of taste and smell.

4 | MEATLESS MAINS

RUBY SHAKSHUKA

Serves: 4
Eat freshly made
Per serving: 249 cals, 15 g carbs

With its creamy poached eggs nestling in a luscious tomato and red pepper ragout, shakshouka (Arabic slang for a mush) is an Israeli breakfast favourite that also makes a wonderful brunch or lunch. It's filling yet surprisingly low carb. Peppers are packed with vitamin C, and tomatoes contain lycopene for prostate health.

2 medium red onions

1 large clove garlic

2 tbsp extra virgin olive oil

2 red pointed sweet peppers

1 bay leaf

½ tsp ras el hanout or cumin seeds

pinch of cayenne, chilli flakes, hot paprika, or harissa

1 tsp fine sea salt

10 grinds black pepper

400 g tin Italian chopped tomatoes

4 large free range eggs

To serve

100 g (3 oz) crumbled feta

1 tbsp coarsely chopped flat-leaf parsley

extra virgin olive oil

Aleppo pepper or chilli flakes

Peel and finely chop the onions and garlic then cook gently in a 20-23 cm (8-9") sauté pan with the oil and a pinch of salt, covered, until very soft and golden, about 8 minutes, stirring occasionally.

Meanwhile, trim and quarter the peppers, remove the pith and seeds then cut into 1 cm (½") squares. Add the peppers to the softened onions and cook together for 5 minutes until the peppers are tender and the onions beginning to colour.

Add the bay leaf and spices, stir well, then add tomatoes and seasonings. Simmer until the mixture is thick but still juicy. At this stage it can be left, covered for up to an hour before reheating.

Remove the bay leaf and make 4 small wells in the simmering tomato mixture. Crack the eggs into a small cup then carefully tip each one into a well and season lightly with salt and pepper.

Cover the pan and poach gently until the eggs are just set, about 5 minutes (they'll continue to cook even off the heat.)

Sprinkle with feta and parsley, then drizzle with a little of the extra virgin oil. Serve with flatbread (see page 66) or pita, and a tiny bowl of Aleppo pepper or chilli flakes for those who like some extra heat.

EGGS are good for the brain and nervous system, eyes, skin, blood and immune system. Eaten in moderation, they don't appear to raise "bad" cholesterol in most people. Although the white contains more protein, most of the vitamins and other nutrients are in the yolk. In Britain, eggs with a red Lion stamp come from hens vaccinated against salmonella, and are considered safe to eat even if uncooked.

> Pictured on previous page

EMERALD SHAKSHUKA

Serves: 4
Eat freshly made
Per serving: 195 cals, 9 g carbs

A vibrant, vitamin-packed twist on the more typical tomato-based shakshuka. Almost any mix of greens will do - in the Middle East they use wild greens and radish leaves. We like a mixture of baby spinach and Swiss chard with lots of fresh herbs.

white part of a medium leek
2 fat spring onions
1-2 jalapeños or green chillies
1 tbsp extra virgin olive oil
generous nut of butter
3 cloves garlic
150 g pack baby spinach
200 g (7 oz) Swiss chard,
    shredded kale,
    or young beetroot tops
½ tsp fine sea salt
10 grinds black pepper
4 tbsp frozen petits pois
    or peas
1 tsp cornflour
2 tbsp vegetable stock
    or water
4 free range eggs

To serve
100 g (3 oz) crumbled feta
10 grinds black pepper
fresh dill, thyme,
    or oregano
½ tsp sumac
extra virgin olive oil
Aleppo pepper or chilli flakes

Trim and thinly slice the leeks, spring onions and jalapeños. Heat the oil and butter in a medium non-stick or cast iron frying pan. Add the leeks, white part of the spring onions, jalapeño, and a pinch of salt. Crush the peeled garlic in a press and add to the pan. Cover and cook gently for 5-8 minutes over medium heat until the vegetables are soft.

Gradually add the greens – as they wilt, they'll all fit in the pan – then sprinkle lightly with salt to preserve their vivid colour. Cook for 2-3 minutes, then add the peas and the green part of the spring onions. Mix the cornflour with the water or stock and stir it into the vegetables. Simmer, uncovered, for 5 minutes or until the greens are tender. The mixture can now be left at room temperature for up to 2 hours.

Make 4-6 small wells in the simmering sauce. Crack the eggs into a small cup then carefully tip each one into a well, then season lightly with salt and black pepper.

Cover the pan and poach gently until the eggs are just set, 5 minutes (they will continue to cook off the heat).

Sprinkle with the feta, sumac and snipped fresh herbs, and drizzle with extra virgin olive oil. Serve with warm flatbread (see page 66) or pita, and a tiny bowl of Aleppo pepper or chilli flakes for those who like a bit of extra heat.

JUDI'S TIPS: use a pair of kitchen tongs to toss the greens with the oil while wilting them. Gently massaging chopped kale leaves with your fingers for a minute or two before cooking breaks down the cell walls, which helps them cook more quickly. Rinsing the massaged leaves before cooking reduces their bitterness.

> Pictured on previous page

ROASTED VEGETABLE KUGEL

Serves: 6-8
Keeps: 3 days in the fridge
Freeze: 3 months
Per serving: 151 cals, 13 g carbs

Inspired by Ashkenazi cuisine and the flavours of the Mediterranean, this satisfying gratin is bursting with flavour. It makes a hearty side dish and served with salad is a meal in itself.

We've replaced the traditional margarine and matzah meal with heart-healthy olive oil and oats. Aubergines contain the antioxidant nasunin, particularly in the skin and outer flesh. Omit the za'atar if someone is allergic to sesame.

---

3 medium aubergines
1 sweet pointed red pepper
2 tbsp olive or rapeseed oil
1 large onion
2 tbsp extra virgin olive oil
2 cloves garlic
2 large eggs
1 tsp za'atar
sprig of thyme
    or ½ tsp dried oregano
20 grinds black pepper
2 tbsp oats
100 g (3½ oz) extra mature
    cheddar
2 tbsp grated parmesan
150 g (5 oz) baby plum
    or cherry tomatoes

Preheat the oven to 220°C/Gas 7 and line a large baking tray with foil.

Cut the trimmed, unpeeled aubergines into 3 cm (1½") cubes and the trimmed and seeded peppers into 3 cm (1½") wide strips. Transfer the vegetables to the prepared tray, drizzle with the olive oil then toss them with your fingers so they're well coated.

Roast the aubergines and peppers for 30-35 minutes, shaking the tin halfway through, until very tender and beginning to brown at the edges.

Quarter, peel, and thinly slice the onion. Warm the extra virgin olive oil in a sauté pan and cook the onion with a pinch of salt, covered, until very soft, 5-8 minutes.

Crush the peeled garlic through a press and add to the onions, then cook gently, uncovered, for 10 minutes, stirring occasionally, until the onions are beautifully caramelised and a rich golden brown.

Whisk the eggs, herbs and other seasonings in a medium bowl until frothy. Grate the cheese then add half of it to the eggs, followed by the vegetables and oats. Mix well with a fork.

When ready to bake the kugel, preheat the oven to 180°C/Gas 4. Lightly oil the bottom and sides of a gratin dish or pan and add the egg mixture. Scatter with the remaining cheese then nestle the halved tomatoes on top. Bake for 35 minutes until a rich golden brown.

HERBED WHOLE GRAIN TARTLET CASES

Serves: 8
Keeps: 3 days in the fridge
Freeze: 3 months
Per serving: 246 cals, 22 g carbs

Savoury tartlets are wonderful for a special lunch or light supper. Homemade pastry is surprisingly quick and easy to make, and so much more flavourful (and healthier) than most store-bought pre-baked shells. A spoonful of olive oil gives this lightly herbed pastry a melt-in-the-mouth texture. The unfilled pastry cases can be frozen in their tins for up to a month, before or after par-baking.

This recipe makes eight tartlet cases, but can also be used for one large tart baked in a 25cm (10") metal or ceramic flan dish. The pastry and method for filling and baking is much the same for the trio of fillings that follow so choose your favourite – or push the boat out and make some of each!

125 g (4 oz) granary, seeded, or whole grain flour
125 g (4 oz) plain flour
½ tsp sea salt
1 tsp dried mixed herbs
1 tsp mustard powder
130 g (4 ½ oz) cold butter
1 large egg
1 tsp wine or cider vinegar
1 tbsp extra virgin olive oil

Have ready eight 10 cm (4") loose-bottomed tartlet cases or mini flan dishes. Put all the dry ingredients into the food processor. Cut the butter into small pieces then add to the flour mixture and process until there are no particles bigger than a pea.

Whisk the egg, vinegar, and oil together in a jug, then with the motor running, pour the egg mixture down the feed tube. Process just until the mixture starts to cling together in little balls.

Tip the dough out onto a board, knead lightly to form a smooth ball then flatten it into a disc, wrap in clingfilm and chill for at least half an hour, or freeze for up to 1 month.

Place the chilled dough between 2 large sheets of cling-film and roll out into a 35 cm (14") circle about 4mm (⅛") thick. Cut out 12 cm (5") circles of dough and press them into the base and up the sides of the ungreased tins, patching and re-rolling the dough as needed – if it becomes too sticky to roll, pop it in the freezer for 5-10 minutes. Prick the pastry cases all over with a fork then chill for 15-30 minutes, or freeze until ready to par-bake.

To par-bake, put a large baking sheet in the oven and preheat it to 200°C/Gas 6. Place the chilled pastry-lined tins on the hot baking sheet and bake for 10-15 minutes until golden and dry to the touch. The cases can now be filled and baked, or frozen in their tins.

JUDI'S TIP: in a pinch, you can use bought short-crust pastry for the following recipes. You'll get the health benefits of the vegetables in the filling though not the whole grains, and of course the pastry won't be as mouthwatering.

> Pictured overleaf

SPINACH & GOATS' CHEESE TARTLETS

Serves: 8
Keeps: 3 days in the fridge
Freeze: 1 month
Per serving: 388 cals, 29 g carbs

Crisp and tender pastry with a light and tasty filling. French-style goats' cheese (fromage de chèvre) gives the best results, but feta also works well. If you're making one large tart rather than 8 tartlets, you may need to bake it for an extra 5 minutes or so until the filling is set.

8 par-baked Herbed Whole Grain
  Tartlet Cases (page 102)

1 tbsp extra virgin olive oil
400-450 g bag baby spinach
½ tsp sea salt
2 cloves garlic
3 eggs
3 tbsp snipped dill, chives,
  or tarragon
10 grinds black pepper
large pinch ground nutmeg
150 ml (5 fl oz) fromage frais,
  quark or Greek yoghurt
175 g (6 oz) finely chopped
  goats' cheese or feta

Heat the oil in a wok or sauté pan and add half the spinach and the garlic, crushed in a press. Sprinkle with half the salt, then cook over brisk heat, tossing with kitchen tongues until the spinach has wilted, then add the rest of the spinach and salt. Cook for another 2-3 minutes until all the spinach has wilted and its liquid has boiled off.

Whisk the eggs in a medium bowl then add your spinach and the remaining filling ingredients. If your cooked spinach doesn't mix in easily with the egg mixture, snip it into short lengths in the bowl using a pair of cooking scissors (I find this less fiddly than chopping it before cooking). Do the same thing with the cheese if some of the pieces are too big. The filling can now be kept in the fridge, covered, for up to 24 hours.

Preheat the oven to 200°C/Gas 6. Place the tartlet cases on a large baking sheet and divide the filling between them. Bake for 20 minutes, then reduce the heat to 190°/Gas 5 and bake for a further 10 minutes or until the filling is firm to gentle touch. Serve warm or at room temperature. May be reheated at 180°C/Gas 4 for 5-10 minutes until warm.

WHOLE GRAINS can help prevent weight gain by making you feel full for longer. Eaten three times a day, grains such as oats, wheat, barley and spelt can help lower your risk of heart disease by more than 20%.

> Pictured overleaf

THYME & MUSHROOM TARTLETS

Serves: 6-8
Keeps: 3 days in the fridge
Freeze: 3 months
Best served freshly baked
Per serving: 327 cals, 28 g carbs

Mushrooms and thyme – a marriage made in heaven. Chestnut or a mixture of wild mushrooms are tastiest, but if there's a bargain offer on what supermarkets call "breakfast" mushrooms, go for those instead. It's essential to brown the mushrooms thoroughly for the best flavour.

8 par-baked Herbed Whole Grain
   Tartlet Cases (page 102)

2 shallots
2 tbsp extra virgin olive oil
2 cloves of garlic
225 g (8 oz) chestnut
   or mixed mushrooms
1 bay leaf
1 tbsp reduced-sodium soy sauce
2 large eggs
150 ml (5 fl oz) Greek yoghurt
1 tbsp fresh thyme leaves,
   or 1 tsp dried thyme
½ tsp salt
10 grinds black pepper
generous pinch of nutmeg

To serve
tiny sprigs of thyme

Halve, peel, and chop the shallots. Cook them gently in the olive oil with a pinch of salt and the garlic, crushed in a press, in a medium frying pan for 4-5 minutes until softened.

Slice the mushrooms thinly, add to the shallots with the bay leaf and stir fry until any liquid released has evaporated and the mushrooms are a rich brown, 10-15 minutes. Remove the bay leaf, add the soy sauce and remove from the heat.

Whisk the eggs with the yoghurt, thyme and seasonings, then add the mushrooms. The filling can now be refrigerated, covered, for up to 12 hours.

To fill and bake, preheat the oven to 200°C/Gas 6. Arrange the pastry cases on a large baking tray and divide the filling between them. Bake for 25-30 minutes or until the pastry is golden brown and the filling is firm to gentle touch. Serve warm, decorated with tiny sprigs of thyme. May be reheated at 180°C/Gas 4 for 5-10 minutes until warm.

JUDI'S TIP: for a more intense mushroom flavour, add a tablespoon of dried wild mushrooms soaked, rinsed and drained (see page 11).

> Pictured on previous page

PROVENÇAL TARTLETS

Serves: 6-8
Keeps: 3 days in the fridge
Freeze: 3 months
Best served freshly baked
Per serving: 310 cals, 31 g carbs

All the scents and taste sensations of Provence in mid-summer are captured in these exquisite tartlets. A true taste of the sun. If you're not a lover of olives, just omit them from the filling, or add a couple of anchovy fillets chopped into small pieces.

8 par-baked Herbed Whole Grain
   Tartlet Cases (page 102)

1 large red onion
1 clove of garlic
1 tbsp extra virgin olive oil
2 tsp sundried tomato purée
   or 1 tbsp finely chopped
   sundried tomatoes in olive oil
1 bay leaf
¼ tsp sea salt
15 grinds black pepper
400 g tin chopped tomatoes
1 tbsp fresh basil leaves
   or 1 tsp dried basil
200 g (7 oz) pitted Kalamata
   or herb-marinated olives

To serve
sprigs of fresh basil

Gently sauté the onion and garlic in the olive oil in a 20 cm (8") sauté pan – keep the lid on for 5 minutes, then uncover and cook gently for another 8-10 minutes until a rich gold and beginning to brown.

Add the tomato purée, bay leaf, salt and pepper, stir well, then add the chopped tomatoes. Stir well, then simmer briskly for 5 minutes over medium heat.

Add the olives, and simmer for a further 5 minutes. The mixture should be juicy but not sloppy. Add the basil then taste, adding more salt if necessary. Leave until cool then remove the bay leaf. Taste the mixture, adding a pinch of sugar if it's a little too sharp.

To fill and bake, preheat the oven to 200°C/Gas 6. Arrange the tartlet cases on a large baking tray and divide the filling between them and bake for 20-30 minutes until the crust is golden. Serve warm, garnished with fresh basil. May be reheated at 180°C/Gas 4 for 5-10 minutes until warm.

TOMATOES are unusual in being more nutritious when cooked than raw. They're rich in vitamin C and lycopene, an antioxidant that protects the lining of the blood vessels and helps lower blood pressure. Recent research suggests a possible link between lycopene and a reduced risk of prostate cancer. It's absorbed best when eaten with fat, so tomatoes and olive oil are a great combination.

> Pictured on previous page

ROASTED VEGETABLE TIAN

Serves: 4-6
Keeps: 2 days in the fridge
Freeze: 3 months
Per serving: 150 cals, 28 g carbs

Mediterranean vegetables in a herbed tomato sauce topped with crisp, golden potatoes. Baked and served in mini gratin dishes or ramekins, the tian makes a stylish vegan course. You can also omit the topping and serve the tian as a side dish.

2 medium carrots
1 red onion
1 small sweet potato
1 red or orange pepper
1 medium fennel bulb
1 courgette
1 aubergine
3 cloves garlic
2 tbsp extra virgin olive oil
½ tsp salt

For the sauce
1 tsp fresh oregano or thyme,
   or a pinch of dried
   herbes de Provence
120 ml (4 fl oz) vegetable stock
400 g tin chopped tomatoes
handful fresh basil leaves
   or 1 tsp dried basil
2 cloves garlic
handful fresh parsley
10 grinds black pepper
½ tsp salt

For the topping
3 medium potatoes
2 tsp olive oil
sprigs fresh thyme or oregano

Preheat the oven to 190°C/Gas 5. Line a large roasting tin with foil for easy clean up. Peel the carrots, onion and sweet potato, then trim and chop all the vegetables into 3 cm (1") cubes. Leave the garlic whole and unpeeled.

Transfer the vegetables and garlic to the roasting tin, add the oil and salt, then mix with your hands or a large spoon so everything is nicely coated. Roast for 30-40 minutes until tinged with brown, turning them over halfway through.

While the vegetables are roasting make the topping. Bring a large pan of water to the boil with a teaspoon of salt. Cut the unpeeled potatoes into 3 mm (⅛") slices and boil for 5-8 minutes until slightly softened, then drain.

Mix all the sauce ingredients together. Once the vegetables are roasted, remove the garlic, pour the sauce over them then return the tin to the oven for 25-30 minutes until you have a thick but still juicy mixture.

Spoon the mixture into a baking dish at least 5 cm (2") deep, or divide between 4-6 ramekins or mini gratin dishes for individual-sized servings. Layer the potato slices over the vegetable mixture, brush with the oil then cover tightly with foil.

Bake at 200°C/Gas 6 for 15 minutes, remove the foil and bake, uncovered, for a further 15-20 minutes or until the topping is a lovely golden brown and the potatoes crisp at the edges – if not, place under a hot grill for a few minutes. Scatter with sprigs of the herbs and serve.

JUDI'S TIP: the dish can be topped with the potatoes and refrigerated for up to 24 hours before the final baking. Chilling converts some of the white carbs in the potatoes into so-called resistant starch, which causes less of a spike in blood sugar than if eaten when first cooked.

CONCHIGLIONI AL FORNO

Serves: 6-8
Keeps: 24 hours in the fridge
Freeze: 2 weeks
Leftovers reheat well
in the microwave
Per serving: 224 cals, 28 g carbs

A gratin of giant pasta shells filled with a luscious mixture of vegetables that's equally at home as a family supper or an elegant lunch. We've replaced the traditional ground almonds in the filling with toasted sunflower seeds so it's nut-free, but coarsely chopped almonds, walnuts, or hazelnuts are also delicious. Chilling the filled pasta before baking converts some of the white carbs to resistant starch, a type of fibre that's good for digestive health.

24-30 conchiglioni
   (giant pasta shells) about
   6 cm (2½") in length
200 g (7 oz) cherry
   or plum tomatoes
2 cloves garlic
1 tbsp extra virgin olive oil
1 tsp fresh or dried basil
   or oregano

For the filling

50 g (2 oz) sunflower seeds
2 tbsp olive oil
3 large shallots
225 g (8 oz) mushrooms
1 clove garlic
450 g (1 lb) Swiss chard
   or spinach
50 g (2 oz) grated
   extra mature cheddar
50 g (2 oz) grated parmesan
1 tbsp chopped parsley
1 tbsp snipped chives
½ tsp ground nutmeg
2 tsp sea salt
10 grinds black pepper

Have ready a gratin dish large enough to hold the tightly packed stuffed shells side by side, about 30 × 18 cm (12 × 7"). Cook the shells according to package directions until barely al dente, then drain in a colander and rinse with cold water to stop them cooking. Drain well then toss with a little olive oil to prevent them sticking.

To make the filling, toast the sunflower seeds in a heavy frying pan, shaking frequently, or on a baking sheet in the oven at 180°C/Gas 4 for 5 minutes. When cool, grind or crush to a coarse powder in a blender, food processor or mortar and pestle.

Halve, peel and finely chop the shallots; slice the mushrooms thinly. Heat the oil in a large sauté pan or wok and cook the shallots with a pinch of salt, covered, until soft and golden, about 4 minutes. Add the mushrooms and sauté them over brisk heat until beginning to brown and the liquid has evaporated. Crush 2 of the peeled garlic cloves in a press and add to the pan.

Remove the thick stalks from the chard or spinach, leaving only the leaves. Roll a stack of leaves into a tight bundle then cut into thin shreds, add to the mushrooms, and sauté over brisk heat for 1-2 minutes until wilted. Stir in the ground sunflower seeds or nuts, seasonings and herbs. Save a rounded tablespoon each of cheddar and parmesan for the topping, then add the rest to the filling.

Chop the tomatoes into small pieces and mix with the remaining garlic, peeled and crushed in a press, the herbs, a teaspoon of the extra virgin olive oil, a pinch of salt and a few grinds of black pepper. Spread the tomato mixture over the bottom of the gratin dish.

Stuff each shell with a tablespoon of filling, then arrange in the dish, filling side up. Sprinkle with the remaining cheese and drizzle with the remaining oil. Chill, covered, for up to 24 hours or freeze for up to 2 weeks (defrost before cooking). Bake in a preheated oven at 200°C /Gas 6 for 20 minutes or until bubbling and a rich golden brown, or microwave for 5-8 minutes then brown under the grill.

HORTOPITA WITH CREAMY DILL SAUCE

GREEK-JEWISH SAVOURY PIE

Serves: 6-8
Keeps: 1 day (ready to bake)
Freeze: 3 months (ready to bake)
Per serving: 300 cals, 35 g carbs

Delicate filo pastry filled with fresh herbs, greens and cheese. The recipe hails from the Jewish community of Ioannina in the North of Greece, where cooks would forage wild greens for the filling, and lovingly make their own filo pastry. It can be served as one large dramatic pie, six spirals, or as several small triangles to serve with drinks. Once formed and filled, the hortopita can be frozen or chilled overnight, tightly covered with clingfilm. If someone is allergic to sesame, use nigella seeds (see page 11) instead.

For the creamy dill sauce

225 g (8 oz) Greek yoghurt
½ a finely diced cucumber
2 tsp finely chopped dill
½ tsp salt
1 clove crushed garlic
8 grinds of black pepper

For the hortopita

2 bunches spring onions
900 g (2 lb) Swiss chard,
   leaves, or 500 g (1 lb)
   baby spinach
1 tbsp extra virgin olive oil
2 large eggs
3 tbsp finely chopped dill
½ tsp fine sea salt
20 grinds of black pepper
½ tsp ground or grated nutmeg
225 g (8 oz) crumbled feta
   or Lancashire cheese
12 sheets (about 350 g) filo pastry
olive oil
2-3 tbsp sesame or nigella seeds

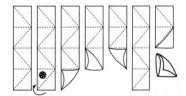

Mix the sauce ingredients together and chill. To make the hortopita, trim and thinly slice the spring onions. Heat the extra virgin olive oil in a frying pan and cook the white part of the spring onions with a pinch of salt for 3 minutes until golden. Finely chop the chard or spinach, add to the pan and cook for another 3-4 minutes. Whisk the eggs and seasonings in a large bowl, then add the green part of the spring onions, cheese, and the contents of the pan. Mix well.

Count out 8 sheets of filo pastry and return the rest to the packet. Quickly cover the 8 sheets with a cloth so they don't dry out. To make one large pie, lightly oil a 25mm (10") pie dish or tin. Brush or spray the first sheet of filo lightly with oil then lay it in the dish with the edges overhanging the sides. Oil another sheet in the same way and lay it on top at a right angle. Repeat with the remaining sheets. Spoon the filling into the centre then bring the overhanging pastry in, pleating it slightly, to partially cover the filling.

To make 6 spirals, oil and layer 8 sheets of filo in a neat rectangle on a board with the long edge facing you. Cut your 8-layer stack into 6 horizontal strips. Spread a band of filling along the length of each strip, leaving about 3 cm (1") along the nearest edge of pastry clear of filling, then roll up into a tight cylinder and coil into a spiral. Transfer your 6 spirals to an oiled baking sheet.

To make 12 triangles, oil, layer and cut the filo into 6 strips as for spirals. Cut each strip in half vertically so you now have 12 shorter strips. Place a tablespoon of filling at the end of each, then fold into triangles (see diagram, left). Transfer your triangles to an oiled baking sheet.

To bake all shapes: preheat the oven to 200°C/Gas 6. Lightly brush or spray the top of the pastry with oil then sprinkle with the seeds. Bake for 30-40 minutes or until a rich golden brown. Transfer to a cooling rack so the bottom stays crisp. Serve warm with the sauce.

> Pictured on previous page

MELTING POT CHOLENT

Serves: 8-10
Keeps: 3 days in the fridge
Freeze: 3 months
Per serving: 192 cals, 33 g carbs

To Ashkenazim this traditional Sabbath casserole, slow-cooked overnight typically includes sink-to-the-bottom-of-your-stomach ingredients like fatty brisket and white potatoes to ward off the cold in the shtetls of Eastern Europe. To Sephardim in the warmth of the Mediterranean, it is dfina or adafina, with ingredients based on the local lighter foods – sorrel, chickpeas, and lots of spices. Our delicious vegan version draws inspiration from both traditions.

Pearled spelt has a delicious nutty taste and creamy texture. It's very digestible and particularly rich in vegetable protein, dietary fibre and a whole host of vitamins and minerals. If you plan to serve the cholent for lunch on Shabbat, start soaking the beans on Thursday afternoon, and put the cholent in the oven to bake shortly before Shabbat begins.

150 g dried mixed beans

100 g dried chickpeas

2 tbsp olive oil

2 large red onions

200 g (7 oz) pearled spelt, or pearl barley (see page 11)

white part of a fat leek

3 sticks celery

2 large cloves garlic

1 medium sweet potato

1 tbsp fennel seeds

2 tbsp tomato purée

2 bay leaves

1 tbsp paprika

1 tbsp ground ginger

1 litre (2 pints) vegetable stock

4 tbsp reduced-sodium soy sauce

2 tsp sea salt

3 medium carrots

15 grinds black pepper

1 tbsp finely chopped parsley

At least 12 hours before cooking, cover the beans and chickpeas with plenty of water and leave to soak.

An hour or so before Shabbat begins, preheat the oven to 120°C/Gas ½. You'll need a large, ovenproof casserole with a well-fitting lid – enamelled cast iron is ideal. Peel and finely chop the onions then fry them gently with the oil and a pinch of salt in the covered casserole, stirring occasionally for 10-12 minutes until soft and golden.

While the onions are cooking, cover the spelt or barley with boiling water. Drain and rinse the beans, chickpeas and spelt or barley. Finely chop the leek, celery and peeled garlic, and cut the peeled sweet potato into bite-sized chunks. Add the fennel seeds and garlic to the onion, cook for a minute, then stir in the tomato purée followed by the spices and all the vegetables except the carrots.

Stir well, then add the stock and soy sauce, mixing to incorporate any residue at the bottom of the pan. Finally, add the spelt, beans, and chickpeas – the stock should just cover them, if not add a little extra water. Bring to a simmer, cover and transfer to the oven.

Shortly before Shabbat begins, stir in the peeled and diced carrots, and leave to cook undisturbed with the lid on until lunchtime the next day. Before serving, taste the cholent, adding a dash more soy sauce if needed, then sprinkle with the pepper and parsley.

ROASTED VEGETABLE PIZZETTE

Serves: 6-8

Eat freshly baked

Freeze: uncooked dough 2 months
(defrost overnight before using.)

Per serving: 263 cals, 36 g carbs

Personal pizzas are fun to make – prepare the dough and toppings ahead, then let everyone build and bake their own. Feel free to use other toppings such as sliced mushrooms, courgettes, mozzarella, or anchovies. We like to add wilted spinach or a handful of rocket just before serving. For the crispiest crust, bake the pizzette on preheated pizza stones or heavy baking sheets. For a shortcut, use ready-made wholemeal flatbreads for the base.

For the dough

110 g (4oz) wholemeal bread flour

170 g (6 oz) extra strong bread
flour (Canadian is best)
plus extra as needed

1 tsp instant yeast

1 tsp honey

175 ml (6 fl oz) warm water

60 ml (2 fl oz) olive oil

1 tsp salt

For the topping

1 red pepper

1 yellow or orange pepper

2 small red onions

1 tbsp olive oil

½ tsp fine sea salt

1 tsp dried oregano
or Italian herbs

20 pitted Kalamata olives

10 grinds black pepper

10-12 cherry tomatoes

120 -150 g pack baby spinach

1 tsp extra virgin olive oil

1 clove garlic

Put the flour and yeast into a food processor or stand mixer. With the motor running, add the water, oil, salt, and honey, and mix until no flour is visible and a ball of dough forms that leaves the sides of the bowl clean. If the dough won't cohere into a ball, add 1-2 tsp water and mix again. If it sticks to the spindle or beater, add more flour, 1 tablespoon at a time, until it leaves the sides of the bowl clean.

Tip the dough onto a work surface, knead for 30 seconds then slap it down onto your worktop 10 times – this develops the gluten and ensures a good texture, as well as being an excellent way of venting pent-up frustration. Put a few drops of oil in a plastic bag, add the dough, close the bag and leave for 1 hour at warm room temperature until doubled in bulk. It can now be chilled, frozen, or baked.

Place a pizza stone or 2 heavy baking sheets in a cold oven and heat to 200°C/Gas 6. Cut the trimmed peppers and onion into thin strips and toss them in a bowl with the olive oil and salt. Spread them out on a large baking tray or roasting tin and roast for 30 minutes, then remove from the oven.

Increase the oven temperature to 250°C/Gas 10. Divide the risen dough into 6 balls and coat both sides with flour. Cover with a cloth and leave to rest for 10 minutes. Halve the tomatoes.

Cut two sheets of baking paper slightly larger than the pizza stone or baking sheets. Roll or stretch each ball of dough into a 15-20 cm (5 × 8") oval. Lay 3 ovals side by side on each sheet of paper and top with the vegetables, olives, herbs, and black pepper. Using a pizza paddle or cold baking sheet slide the pizzette and paper onto the preheated stone or baking sheet while wearing oven gloves.

Bake the pizzette for 8-10 minutes or until the crust is puffy and golden. Meanwhile, wilt the spinach with the garlic, crushed in a press, and a pinch of salt, in the extra virgin olive oil for 2-3 minutes. Transfer the pizzette to a cooling rack and slide the paper out from underneath them to keep the base crisp. Add the spinach and serve.

5 | FISH

FENNEL
CURED SALMON

FENNEL OR BEETROOT CURED SALMON

Serves: 10-12
Keeps: 5 days in the fridge
Freeze: 3 months
Per serving: 105 cals, 1 g carbs

Home-cured salmon is surprisingly easy to make and far more economical than buying smoked salmon. Serve it on bite-sized squares of rye bread topped with Greek yoghurt with a dash of horseradish and Dijon mustard as an appetiser, or with capers and Quick Cucumber Pickles (page 71) as part of a buffet or brunch.

Salmon is rich in omega-3 for brain and heart health, and can reduce the risk of angina, heart attack and dementia.

1 tail fillet of salmon,
   550-700 g (1 lb 3 oz-1 lb 8 oz),
   skin left on
1 tbsp fennel seeds
1 rounded tbsp coarse sea salt
1 tbsp brown sugar
¼ tsp white pepper
10 grinds black pepper
bunch of fresh dill

Ask your fishmonger for their freshest, best quality salmon. Check the fish for pin bones, trim off any excess skin and fat at the sides and tail, then pat dry with paper towels.

To make the curing mixture, crush the fennel seeds with a mortar and pestle or a rolling pin. Chop the dill finely then mix with the fennel, salt, sugar, and peppers. Tip the mixture into a plastic container or non-metallic dish large enough to hold the fish. Lay the salmon flesh side down on top of the cure, then turn it over and pat the mixture onto the flesh side, making sure the ends are also coated.

Cover the container with a lid or clingfilm then leave at room temperature for 30 minutes to kick-start the curing process then transfer it to the fridge.

After 24 hours, turn the fish over and leave for a further 24 hours (liquid may have collected in the container which is normal). Remove the fish, rinse very briefly then pat dry. To serve, carve into very thin slices with a long, sharp knife, starting at the tail end.

BEETROOT CURED SALMON

Use the same ingredients and method as above but replace the fennel and dill with a finely chopped, cooked (not pickled) beetroot.

ZA'ATAR CRUSTED FISH
WITH PISTACHIO & CITRUS CREME

Serves: 6
Keeps: 1 day in the fridge
Sauce keeps: 3 days
in the fridge
Do not freeze.
Per serving: 512 cals, 12 g carbs

A creamy pistachio sauce, vibrant with fresh citrus juice and zest, makes a delicious vegan alternative to Hollandaise sauce, and a perfect foil for the fish. It's inspired by a recipe Evelyn Rose developed with her colleague, Sula Leon.

This is a great dinner party dish as most of it can be prepared several hours ahead, leaving only the fish to be topped and baked before serving. Use a teaspoon of chopped fresh thyme instead of the za'atar if anyone is allergic to sesame.

---

6 skinless cod, haddock,
  salmon, or halibut fillets,
  140-170 g (5-6 oz) each
  and about 2 cm (¾") thick
½ tsp fine sea salt
10 grinds black pepper
1-2 tbsp Easy Lemon Mayo
  (page 76)

For the crust
185 g (6 oz) shelled pecans
1 tbsp za'atar
4 tbsp snipped fresh chives
2 tbsp melted butter
finely grated zest of ½ a lemon
pinch fine sea salt

For the sauce
100 g (3½ oz) shelled pistachios
4 tbsp extra virgin olive oil
½ tsp fine sea salt
finely grated zest of 1 lemon
  and 1 lime
juice of 2 tangerines
  or 1 large orange (about 5 tbsp)
pinch of sugar or erythritol
juice of ½ a lemon
1 tbsp yuzu (see page 11)
  or grapefruit juice

Lightly oil a rimmed baking tin or oven proof dish large enough to hold the fish in one layer without crowding. Check the fillets for small bones, then season with the salt and pepper, and spread with a thin layer of mayonnaise. Arrange the fillets in the baking tin or dish.

To make the crust, grind the nuts in a food processor for 10-15 seconds until they look like coarse sand. Transfer to a bowl and mix with the rest of the crust ingredients. Cover each fillet with an even layer of the crust mixture, patting it on well.

To make the sauce, chop the pistachios in a food processor. Add the rest of the sauce ingredients and process for 10-15 seconds until creamy but with a little texture left.

About half an hour before the meal, preheat the oven to 220°C/Gas 7. Fifteen minutes before serving, put in the fish and bake for 8-12 minutes until the flesh is opaque when gently parted with a pointed knife and the crust is nicely browned. Serve warm with the pistachio sauce.

GRILLED SALMON WITH AVOCADO SALSA

Serves: 6
Keeps: 2 days in the fridge
Do not freeze
Per serving: 471 cals, 12 g carbs

Take some centre steaks of prime salmon, anoint them with a little olive oil or butter, cook to golden succulent perfection under a gentle grill, then bring to the table with a dish of vegetables and a crisp green salad. Result: a meal which will rival the best efforts of any restaurant.

Grilling is one of the simplest cooking techniques but, like most simple things, must be carried out with care and attention to detail. Start with very fresh, good thick pieces of fish. This allows the surface to turn a lovely golden brown while keeping the delicate flesh juicy. Butter gives a better colour and flavour, but olive oil can be used instead.

6 salmon steaks,
  175-200 g (6-7 oz) each
  and 2-2.5 cm (¾ -1") thick
fine sea salt
freshly-ground black pepper
a little brown or white flour
  for dredging the fish
50 g (2 oz) butter
  or 3 tbsp extra virgin olive oil

For the salsa
2 ripe avocados
½ bunch spring onions
1 sweet pointed red pepper
juice of 1-1½ limes (2 tbsp)
½ tsp fine sea salt
10 grinds black pepper
½ tsp ground coriander
1 jalapeño or similar green chilli

To serve
6 wedges of lime

An hour or so before serving, prepare the avocado salsa. Halve the red pepper and jalapeño, remove the pith and seeds then chop finely. Trim and thinly slice the white and green part of the spring onions. Pit, quarter and peel the avocados then cut into small cubes and mix gently with the other salsa ingredients. Cover and chill until needed.

Preheat the grill to medium. Lightly salt and pepper the washed and dried fish. Melt the butter under the grill in a grill pan or heavy baking tin large enough to hold the fish in one layer.

When the butter has melted and before it starts to brown, add the fish then immediately turn it over so it is coated with butter on both sides. If using olive oil, warm it for 1-2 minutes under the grill before adding the fish and turning it over as before.

Grill for 2 minutes then turn the fish over, dredge lightly with flour (this promotes browning), baste with the pan juices and grill gently for a further 8 - 10 minutes depending on the thickness of the fish, basting again halfway, until the fish flakes easily. Transfer to a serving plate, top with salsa and serve with the lime wedges.

GRILLED HALIBUT WITH LEMON & ALMONDS

For a special occasion, use halibut steaks instead of salmon. Grill as before then lift the fish out of the grill pan, and add 2 rounded tbsp of flaked almonds to the pan juices, return the pan to the grill for a minute or two until the nuts are golden, then pour in 3 tbsp freshly squeezed lemon juice, add a good pinch of sea salt and 10 grinds of black pepper, stir well, then spoon over the fish.

HERB ROASTED COD ON A BED
OF FENNEL & NEW POTATOES

Serves: 4-6
Keeps: 1 day in the fridge
Do not freeze
Per serving: 472 cals, 42 g carbs

Once considered a rather boring fish, roasted cod is succulent and delicious – a far cry from the bland, watery offering Jackie and I remember from school dinners at Manchester High School for Girls. Perhaps we have finally made our peace with cod.

Roasting the fish under a light crust is the key to perfectly cooked cod, bursting with flavour. The result is succulent fish beneath a crisp lemony crust. To turn it into a dinner party dish, we serve the fish on a bed of warm vegetables tossed with a vinaigrette dressing, a fabulous combination. Use small salad potatoes rather than larger starchy ones which can become mushy.

Like all white fish, cod is a good source of protein and vitamins B and D. Chilling the potatoes produces resistant starch, reducing their sugar spike, or glycaemic load. The herbs and dressing provide antioxidants and are anti-inflammatory.

4-6 skinless cod fillets,
  each weighing about
  150 g (5 oz) and at least
  2.5 cm (1") thick

1 tbsp extra virgin olive oil

salt and black pepper

1 tbsp lemon mayonnaise
  (page 76)

For the herb crust

2 slices brown bread

generous handful of fresh parsley,

½ tsp fresh tarragon
  or fines herbes

1 tbsp fresh thyme or a pinch
  of dried thyme

zest of 1 lemon

½ tsp fine sea salt

5 grinds black pepper

1 clove garlic

50 g (2 oz) very soft butter

For the vinaigrette

3 tbsp extra virgin olive oil

1 tbsp wine or cider vinegar

1 tsp lemon juice

1 tsp mustard powder

pinch of paprika

¼ tsp salt

8 grinds black pepper

1 clove garlic

For the vegetable bed

900 g (2 lb) small new
  potatoes

2 medium fennel bulbs

2 tsp extra virgin olive oil

225 g (8 oz) cherry tomatoes

chopped dill or parsley

2 long pointed sweet red
  peppers

Check the fish for bones, then wash, drain in a colander and sprinkle lightly with salt and pepper. Put the olive oil in an oval or rectangular ovenproof gratin dish large enough to hold the fish in one layer without crowding. Spread a thin layer of mayonnaise over each fillet then arrange in the dish.

Put all the crust ingredients except the butter into a food processor and process until finely chopped. Pulse in the butter. Spoon an even layer of the crust mixture on the top of each fillet and press lightly with the back of the spoon.

To make the vinaigrette, smash the clove of garlic with the side of a knife then remove the skin. Put the garlic and the other dressing ingredients in a screw-top jar and shake well.

Put the unpeeled potatoes in a pan of water to cover, halving any large ones. Bring to the boil, add a teaspoon of salt, and simmer for 8-10 minutes or until tender. Trim the root off the fennel, slice the bulb thinly and add to the potatoes. Simmer for a further 2-3 minutes, then drain.

Half an hour before serving, preheat the oven to 220°C/Gas 7. Roast the fish in the oven for 10-12 minutes, or until the centre of each fillet has lost its translucency (check by gently parting the flesh with the point of a knife).

While the fish is cooking, trim, seed, and cut the sweet peppers into ½ cm (¼") dice. Heat the 2 teaspoons of olive oil in a wide nonstick frying pan, and add the potatoes and fennel. Sauté over high heat for 5-8 minutes, shaking the pan from time to time, until the potatoes are lightly browned. Add the tomatoes and sauté for another minute. Finally, add the diced red peppers and the well-shaken dressing. Mix gently.

Tip the vegetables onto a platter, arrange the fish on top, and garnish with fresh herbs.

CREAMY FISH PIE WITH LEMON & DILL

Serves: 6 generously
Dish can be prepared
up to 24 hours in advance
then baked as required.
Per serving: 345 cals, 32 g carbs

30G. BUTTER OR
2 tbsp OLIVE OIL

½ tsp olive oil
1 small onion
8 black peppercorns
2 bay leaves
½ tsp salt
2 parsley sprigs
300 g (11 oz) cod or haddock fillet
425 ml (15 fl oz) milk
300 g (11 oz) skinless salmon fillet
squeeze of lemon juice

For the sauce
white part of a leek
2 rounded tbsp flour
½ tsp salt
20 grinds black pepper
shake of white pepper
125 g (4 oz) baby spinach
3 tbsp snipped fresh dill
squeeze fresh lemon juice
50 g (2 oz) grated
   extra mature cheddar

For the topping
750g (1 lb 10 oz) large potatoes
350g (12 oz) cauliflower
6 tbsp milk
25 g (1 oz) butter
¼ tsp ground nutmeg
1 tsp fine sea salt
pinch of white pepper

A comforting dish packed with an array of vegetables, concealed under a golden cauliflower and mashed potato topping, a stealthy way of helping veggie-averse kids to eat their five-a-day.

Lightly oil a gratin dish 28-30 cm (11"-12") long and at least 5 cm (2") deep. Peel and thinly slice the onion.

Put the fish in a wide pan, preferably non-stick, with the onion, bay leaf, peppercorns, salt and parsley. Add the milk, lemon juice and just enough water to cover. Bring slowly to the boil then remove from the heat, cover and leave to stand for 10 minutes although longer will do no harm.

Remove the fish from the pan then strain the poaching liquid into a measuring jug. There should be about 430 ml (15 fl oz). If necessary, make up the difference with some extra milk. Remove any skin and small bones from the fish, then flake the flesh very coarsely with a fork and arrange in an even layer in the gratin dish.

To make the sauce, put the butter and the trimmed, thinly sliced leek into a saucepan and cook for 5 minutes. Add the flour, stirring well, and cook for 2 minutes, then pour in the milk and seasonings, whisking constantly. Reduce the heat and bubble for 2 minutes until thickened. Off the heat, stir in the spinach, dill, lemon juice and cheddar. Pour over the fish.

To make the topping, peel and quarter the potatoes. Put them in a pan with enough water to cover and a teaspoon of salt. Bring to the boil and cook for 10 minutes. Break the cauliflower into florets, add to the potatoes and boil for a further 10 minutes or until the potatoes and cauliflower are tender when pierced with a sharp knife. Drain the vegetables then return to the pan. Over low heat, trickle the milk down the side of the pan. When it begins to steam, add the butter and seasonings, then mash until smooth (easiest with an electric whisk). Spread the topping in an even layer over the fish and mark decoratively with a fork.

Preheat the oven to 190°C/Gas 5. Bake for 30 minutes or until the topping is a rich golden brown and you can just see the filling bubbling at the sides.

CRISPY OVEN-BAKED FISH BALLS

Makes: 9-10 medium patties,
or 40-50 bite-size balls
Per bite-size ball: 41 cals, 2 g carbs

Chopped fried fish is an Anglo-Jewish favourite, perhaps inspired by the fried fish introduced by Sephardi settlers from Spain and Portugal. Instead of the traditional deep frying, we toss the fish balls with a little oil then brown them in a hot oven, a technique known as air-frying. It's lot less messy, a lot more healthy, and doesn't fill the house with the smell of fried fish. Plus there's no panful of hot oil to deal with at the end. What's not to like?

We've replaced the usual matzah meal with heart-healthy oats, protein-packed ground almonds, and omega-3-rich ground flaxseed. Sesame seeds in the coating add crunch but can be omitted if anyone is allergic. We love to serve the fish balls freshly baked with Quick Cucumber Pickles (page 71) and Green Herb Mayonnaise (page 76).

---

1 medium onion

2 large eggs

450 g (1 lb) haddock or hake fillet

450 g (1 lb) cod fillet

2 tsp sea salt

1 rounded tsp sugar or erythritol

10 grinds black pepper

1 tbsp olive oil

1 tbsp ground almonds

1 tbsp ground golden flax seeds

3 tbsp porridge oats

1-2 tbsp oat bran or matzah meal,
    if needed

For the coating

2 heaped tbsp sesame seeds

2-3 slices brown bread
    or matzo meal

3 tbsp olive oil

Ask the fishmonger to mince the fish for you. Otherwise cut the fillets into 2.5 cm (1") chunks and put in the processor in two batches, half-filling the bowl each time. Process for 10-20 seconds until finely chopped then turn into a mixing bowl.

Cut the peeled onion into chunks and put into the food processor with the eggs, seasonings, oil, oats, ground almonds and flaxseed. Process until reduced to a smooth purée then add to the fish and mix thoroughly using a large fork. The mixture can now be kept in the fridge, covered, for up to 12 hours.

To make the coating, tear the bread into pieces then process to fine crumbs in a food processor. Mix the crumbs and sesame seeds together then spread on a nonstick baking tray and place in a cold oven. Set the oven to 220°C /Gas 7 and leave the coating to brown while the oven heats up, 8-10 minutes, shaking the tray halfway through. Transfer the coating to a shallow dish.

To form and coat the fish balls, add the oil to a large baking tray. Form the fish mix into patties about 7 cm (2½") long, 3 cm (1½") wide and 2 cm (¾") thick, or into cocktail balls the size of a large marble. If the mix is too soft to form into balls, add an extra 1-2 tablespoons of oats or oat bran. Pop the fish balls onto the tray and turn to coat both sides with oil then drop them into the coating mixture and shake gently until well coated on all sides. Arrange on the baking tray.

Bake at 220°C/Gas 7 for 15-20 minutes until a rich golden brown on the underside, then turn them over and cook for a further 10-15 minutes until nicely browned on both sides.

MISO GLAZED SALMON

Serves: 4
Keeps: 2 days in the fridge
Per serving: 234 cals, 6 g carbs

A simple but really delicious way to serve salmon, bursting with "umami" flavours. Cooked on a barbecue, the fish takes on a subtle smoky flavour, but the recipe works just as well under a good hot grill. We like to serve it on a bed of brown rice with Stir-Fried Seasonal Greens (page 172).

Miso, a savoury paste made from fermented soya beans, is one of the most delicious ways to get the probiotic benefits of fermented foods, and keeps in the fridge for months. Yuzu juice has a unique citrusy flavour, but a mix of grapefruit, tangerine and lime juice can be used instead. If anyone is allergic to sesame, leave out the shichimi togarashi or sesame seeds.

---

4 salmon fillets
  130-150 g (4 ½-5 oz) each,
  skin on

1 tsp fine sea salt

½ tsp white pepper

For the glaze

2 tbsp miso

1 tsp Dijon mustard

2 tbsp mirin

2 tbsp yuzu juice (see page 11)
  or 1 tbsp each lime, tangerine
  and grapefruit juice

To serve

1 tbsp shichimi togarashi
  (see page 11)
  or 1 tbsp toasted sesame seeds
  mixed with a pinch each
  of sea salt and chilli flakes

Remove any pin bones from the fish, then rinse, drain in a colander and season with the salt and pepper.

Whisk the miso and mustard together in a small bowl then whisk in the mirin and juice. Transfer a third of the mixture to a dipping bowl to serve as a sauce at the table.

Preheat the grill to high, with an oven rack about 10 cm (4") below the element. Line a baking tray with foil and add the salmon, skin side down.

Grill the fish for 5 minutes, then brush each fillet generously with the miso glaze and grill for a further 5 minutes, or until the top is lightly browned and the fish firm to gentle touch and opaque in the middle – check by nicking with a slim pointed knife.

Sprinkle with the shichimi togarashi or sesame seeds, arrange on a serving dish, and serve with the reserved sauce.

SALMON may help prevent dementia, heart attacks, angina, cancer and diabetes. It also has an anti-inflammatory effect, which may reduce the risk of rheumatoid arthritis. Like other oily fish, it lowers the risk of depression, a benefit further boosted by the presence of vitamin B3,

6 | POULTRY & MEAT

FAJITAS & FIXIN'S

Serves: 6-8
Keeps: 1 day in the fridge
Do not freeze
Per serving: 253 cals, 12 g carbs

Throughout the Diaspora, Jewish cooks have embraced local ingredients, techniques, and cuisines, and the community in Dallas is no exception. Long before wraps became ubiquitous in Europe, they were relishing sizzling strips of meat with bite-tender vegetables enveloped in soft warm tortillas, and what Texans call "the fixin's" – condiments and salsa bursting with fresh, bold flavours.

Building a fajita wrap is a fun way of encouraging kids to eat fresh veggies, and using chicken thigh fillets ensures succulent meat that's almost impossible to overcook. Don't use tahini if someone is allergic to sesame.

For the marinade

3 cloves garlic
2 tbsp Worcestershire sauce
juice of a lime
2 tbsp dark soy sauce
10 grinds black pepper
1-2 finely chopped jalapeños
1 tbsp olive oil

For the fajitas

600 g (1lb 5 oz) boneless, skinless chicken thighs
½ tsp fine sea salt
2 tsp olive or coconut oil
2 large red onions
1 red, 1 green, and 1 orange or yellow pepper
1 pack whole wheat wraps or tortillas

For the fixin's

Avocado and Lime Salsa (page 126)
Pico de Gallo (page 77)
lime wedges
coriander leaves
vegan sour cream, or Tahina Sauce (page 77)

Whack the unpeeled garlic with the side of a large knife to release its flavour. Mix all the marinade ingredients, including the garlic, in a bowl or resealable bag. Trim any loose fat from the chicken, open out the thighs then add them to the marinade and turn to coat. Leave for 20 minutes, or up to 24 hours in the fridge.

About 20 minutes before you want to eat, heat a heavy frying pan or ridged grill pan on the stove for 2 minutes. Add the oil, spreading it over the surface with a silicone brush. When very hot add the chicken (it should sizzle – you might want to have a cover or splatter screen to hand) and sear over high heat without moving the chicken for 4-5 minutes. Turn the thighs over and cook for another 4-5 minutes or until a rich brown and cooked all the way through – check by nicking with a sharp knife to make sure the flesh in the centre is opaque. Reduce the heat if the chicken is browning too quickly. Transfer to a baking tray, cover loosely with foil, and leave to rest for 5-10 minutes so the chicken is juicy and easier to carve.

Meanwhile, put the fixin's into small bowls. Halve the onions, peel, and slice into thin crescents. Halve the peppers, seed, and slice into thin strips. Warm the wraps according to package directions.

Heat the pan again until very hot, add the peppers and onions, and stir fry over high heat for 2-3 minutes or until just tender. Add the reserved marinade and boil for 2 minutes. Carve the chicken at an angle into thin strips then add them and any juices to the onions and peppers. Each diner can fill their own wrap with chicken and vegetables topped with the fixin's.

     > Pictured on previous page

CRISPY CHICKEN WITH MELTING LEEKS

Serves: 6-8
Keeps: 3 days in the fridge
Freeze: 3 months
Per serving: 244 cals, 13 g carbs

Crispy chicken thighs roasted, French-style, over a bed of vegetables that melt down into a delicious sauce. Don't be alarmed by the amount of garlic. The cloves are blanched then roasted until transformed into translucent pearls with a sweet, gentle flavour.

Garlic and leek are prebiotics which help lower cholesterol, stabilise blood sugar, and aid circulation. To keep the cholesterol and calories down, we trim most of the skin off the chicken, leaving just enough to keep the flesh moist while cooking.

---

3 heads of garlic,
  or about 2 dozen cloves
½ -1 tsp fine sea salt
10 grinds black pepper
2 tbsp extra virgin olive oil
680 g (1½ lb) leeks
6-8 medium bone-in skin-on
  chicken thighs
2 bay leaves
250 ml (9 fl oz) dry white wine
250 ml (9 fl oz) chicken stock

Preheat the oven to 200°C/Gas 6. Have ready an oven-proof sauté pan or a flameproof metal casserole large enough to hold the chicken joints in a single layer. If you have neither, start the vegetable base in a frying pan on the stove, then transfer it to a roasting tin before adding the chicken.

Separate the garlic into cloves, place them in a saucepan and cover with cold water. Bring to the boil and drain. When cool enough to handle, slip off the skins by cutting off the hard end of each clove, then dry them on paper towels. Trim and thinly slice the white and light green part of the leeks. Heat the oil in the sauté pan or casserole over medium-high heat. When it shimmers, add the leeks, garlic, and a pinch of the salt. Reduce the heat, cover, and cook until the leeks are soft, about 15 minutes, stirring from time to time. Add the bay leaves, wine, and stock, stir well, and bring to the boil.

Trim the loose skin and fat from the chicken (easiest with a pair of kitchen shears). Pat dry with paper towels and season lightly with salt and pepper. Lay the chicken, skin side up, in a single layer on top of the leeks, transfer to the oven, and roast for 30 minutes until the chicken is cooked through and the juices run clear when nicked with a knife in the thickest part of the joint. If the skin isn't crisp, turn on the grill and cook for a further 5-8 minutes. By this time the leeks should be meltingly tender, the garlic soft and sweet, and the chicken crisp on the outside and succulent inside.

GARLIC helps prevent blood clots, may reduce blood pressure and, like leeks, contains inulin, a type of fibre that's great for gut health. Garlic may also reduce LDL cholesterol and help control blood sugar.

FRAGRANT CHICKEN
WITH ORANGES & ALMONDS

Serves: 6-8
Keeps: 2 days in the fridge
Freeze: 2 months
Per serving: 370 cals, 18 g carbs

Tender chicken in a sweet and tangy citrus sauce, this is one of our favourite Evelyn Rose-inspired creations. Oranges are high in vitamin C, vitamin A, folic acid, and the antioxidant hesperidin that can help lower blood pressure and cholesterol. Raisins provide natural sweetness, fibre, and boron, a mineral that may help prevent osteoporosis. For a gluten-free version dust the chicken with cornflour or brown rice flour.

---

2 tbsp plain or spelt flour

1 tsp fine sea salt

10 grinds of black pepper

6-8 chicken thigh fillets

2 tbsp olive oil

3 tbsp blanched halved
   or slivered almonds

For the sauce

4 large oranges

275 ml (10 fl oz) dry white wine
   such as Sauvignon Blanc

150 ml (5 fl oz) strong chicken
   stock or bone broth

grated zest of 1 lemon

1 tbsp thin honey

3 tbsp raisins or sultanas

1 cinnamon stick

2 tsp cornflour mixed to a cream
   with 1 tbsp water

1 tbsp fresh pomegranate seeds

Mix the flour with the salt and pepper. Lightly coat both sides of the chicken with the seasoned flour.

Heat the oil in a large sauté pan. When hot, add the chicken and cook over brisk heat until golden on both sides, about 8 minutes. Nick a thigh to check that there's no sign of pinkness – if there is, cook for another few minutes. Transfer the chicken to a plate. Sauté the almonds in the same pan for 2-3 minutes or until golden brown on both sides, then remove with a slotted spoon and add to the chicken.

Pour off any fat, leaving the flavourful golden brown "fond" at the bottom of the pan. Add the wine and bubble for 3 minutes, stirring to incorporate the fond. Add the juice of 2 oranges, followed by the stock, lemon zest, honey, raisins, and cinnamon. Bring to the boil then add the chicken with any juices. Cover and simmer very gently until the thighs are cooked through, 10 -15 minutes. At this stage the casserole can be refrigerated, covered, for up to 24 hours.

To serve, peel and remove all the pith from the remaining 2 oranges then cut the flesh into sections or thin slices. Bring the chicken and sauce slowly back to the simmer until the chicken is thoroughly heated through, then stir in the cornflour cream and bubble for 3 minutes until the sauce is slightly thickened. Turn off the heat and add the orange sections and pomegranate seeds, then scatter with the almonds. Serve directly from the pan, or transfer the chicken to a warm platter and spoon the sauce over it.

JUDI'S TIP: the casserole can also be reheated in the oven at 180°C/Gas 4 covered, for 25-30 minutes or until bubbling. Add the orange sections, almonds and pomegranate seeds shortly before serving.

KUNG PAO CHICKEN

Serves: 6
Keeps: 1 day in the fridge
Freeze: 1 month
Per serving: 285 cals, 9 g carbs

Legend has it this exquisite stir-fry, sometimes called Sichuan Chicken, harks back to the Qing Dynasty. Centuries later it's still a firm favourite. For a vegan version, use cubes of well-dried extra firm tofu instead of chicken.

Miso, made from fermented soybeans is probiotic, which helps your good gut bacteria. Like other cruciferous vegetables, pak choi has anti-inflammatory properties, and may help protect against cancer.

---

600 g (1 ¼ lb) chicken thigh fillets
1 tbsp reduced-sodium soy sauce
1 tbsp cornflour
2 tbsp coconut or rapeseed oil
1 red and 1 yellow pepper
1 cm (¼") piece of fresh ginger
2-3 baby pak choi
2-3 small dried red chillies,
    or a pinch of chilli flakes
2 tbsp miso (see page 11)
2 tbsp bone broth, stock or water
3 spring onions
3 tbsp roasted cashews or peanuts

Freeze the chicken for 30 minutes until firm, then cut into 2.5cm (1") cubes. Mix the chicken, soy sauce and cornflour together in a bowl and marinate for at least 5 minutes or up to 24 hours in the fridge.

Heat a wok or large sauté pan over high heat until very hot then add the oil, swirling it around the pan. When the oil is almost smoking, add half the chicken, spreading the cubes out in a single layer over the bottom and sides of the wok, then cook without stirring or moving them for 2-3 minutes.

When the underside of the chicken is a rich, golden brown, stir-fry by tossing it with a large metal spoon or wok spatula for a further 2-3 minutes until brown on all sides and cooked through (nick a couple of cubes with a knife to check). Transfer the chicken to a dish with a slotted spoon, leaving behind as much of the oil as possible, then cook the next batch in the same way.

Peel and grate the ginger. Cut the trimmed and seeded peppers, pak choi and spring onions into 2.5cm (1") pieces, keeping the white and leafy green parts of the pak choi and spring onions separate.

Reheat the oil in the wok, scraping the bottom with a large metal spoon or spatula to loosen any residue. When the oil is hot, add the ginger and white parts of the spring onion. Stir-fry over high heat for 10 seconds, then add the white parts of the pak choi and stir-fry for 30 seconds.

Reduce the heat and add the chillies, miso, broth or water, the chicken with any juices, and the green parts of the pak choi and spring onions. Stir fry for 30 seconds to wilt the greens, then add the nuts and turn off the heat. Check the seasoning, add more soy or a pinch of salt if needed, and serve with brown rice or spelt noodles.

PAELLA VALENCIANA

Serves: 6-8
Keeps: 2 days in the fridge
Do not freeze
Per serving: 380 cals, 40 g carbs

Our Valencia-style version uses spelt, a deliciously nutty, creamy biblical grain that's higher in protein and fibre than the traditional short-grain white rice. You don't need a special pan to make paella – a very wide shallow frying pan, ideally 31-38 cm (12-15") will do just fine. For a vegan version, use a handful of chestnut mushrooms and a small jar of marinated artichoke hearts instead of chicken.

350 g (12 oz) pearled spelt
    or pearl barley (page 11)
600 g (1 lb 5 oz) boneless
    chicken thighs
3 tbsp extra virgin olive oil
4 roasted peppers, about ½ a jar
1 whole head of garlic

For the sofrito

3 cloves garlic
1 large onion
2 tsp paprika
4 tbsp tinned chopped tomatoes
½ -1 tsp fine sea salt
pinch of cayenne
good pinch (8-10 threads) saffron
1 litre (1 ¾ pints) strong chicken
    or vegetable stock

To finish

100 ml (3 fl oz) dry white wine
    or stock
10 grinds black pepper
¼ tsp grated nutmeg
3 tbsp frozen peas or petits pois
handful each of baby tomatoes,
    lightly cooked haricots verts
    or green beans, and
    edamame or broad beans
lemon wedges and flat-leaf
    parsley to serve

Cover the spelt or barley with boiling water and leave to soak. Trim 1 cm (½ inch) off the top of the head of garlic to expose the cloves, then remove any loose papery skin.

Cut the chicken thighs into quarters, or in half if you prefer larger pieces. Heat the oil in your pan and when hot add the chicken. Sprinkle with a dash of salt and black pepper, then add the head of garlic, cut side down. Cook over brisk heat for 4-5 minutes, until the chicken is golden brown on both sides and cooked through with no sign of pink in the centre. Transfer to a dish with tongs or a slotted spoon, leaving the oil in the pan. Refrigerate if not serving the paella within an hour.

To make the sofrito, halve, peel and chop the onions as finely as you can. Add to the pan, cover and cook gently for 10 minutes until soft and golden, stirring occasionally. Peel the 3 garlic cloves, crush them in a press and add to the onions along with the tinned tomatoes. Cook, uncovered, for 3-5 minutes, then stir in the paprika, cayenne and saffron and fry gently for a minute or two until fragrant.

Drain the spelt or barley and add to the pan with three-quarters of the stock. Nestle the head of garlic, cut side up, in the centre. Simmer, covered, 25-30 minutes until the spelt is tender but slightly chewy (barley will need about 45 minutes). The paella can be prepared up to this point and left at room temperature, covered, for up to an hour.

Add the wine, remaining stock, black pepper and nutmeg then bubble briskly, uncovered, until most of the liquid has evaporated, 5-10 minutes, shaking the pan from time to time. Nestle the chicken, peppers, cherry tomatoes and your other toppings into the spelt, then cover and cook on the lowest possible heat for 5-10 minutes for the flavours to mingle and the chicken and toppings to heat through. Uncover, and check the seasonings, then add the lemon wedges and parsley and serve with a crisp green salad.

JUDI'S TIPS: if you want soccarat – a crispy layer on the bottom – be sure to shake but not stir during the last 10-15 minutes. For a gluten-free version, use paella or risotto rice instead of spelt.

A TAGINE OF CHICKEN & APRICOTS

Serves: 6
Keeps: 3 days in the fridge
Freeze: 2 months
Per serving: 265 cals, 18 g carbs

Tagines – slow-cooked stews of succulent meat and fruit in a silky, gently spiced sauce– are surely one of the glories of North African Jewish cuisine. A tajine is also the name of an earthenware casserole with a conical lid in which the stew is traditionally cooked but a wide, flame-proof casserole will do fine.

Ras el hanout is a North African spice blend. If you can't find it, use a teaspoon each of ground coriander, ginger, and a pinch of cardamom and cumin, which all have antioxidant properties. Apricots provide fibre and vitamin A, and cinnamon can help control blood sugar and lower cholesterol.

For the spice paste

1 tsp turmeric
1 tsp ground cumin
1 tsp ground cinnamon
1 tbsp ras el hanout (see page 11)
½ tsp fine sea salt
10 grinds black pepper
1-2 tbsp water

6-8 bone-in chicken thighs
2 tbsp blanched almonds
1 large onion
1 tbsp extra virgin olive oil
200 g (7 oz) dried apricots
2 cinnamon sticks
250 ml (9 fl oz) chicken stock
  or bone broth (page 47)
1 tsp cornflour
2 tbsp pomegranate seeds
1 tbsp chopped flat-leaf parsley

Mix the spice paste ingredients together. Remove the skin and any loose fat from the chicken then coat the flesh with the spice paste using a silicone brush or your hands (wear disposable gloves if you prefer). Leave for 20 minutes at room temperature, or up to 24 hours in the fridge.

Set the oven to 160°C/Gas 3. Spread the almonds on a baking tray and put them in the oven to roast for 10-15 minutes as it heats up. When golden brown, remove the nuts but keep the oven on.

Meanwhile, peel and finely chop the onion. Heat the oil in the casserole, add the onion and a pinch of salt and cook gently, covered, for 5-8 minutes until soft. Add the chicken (do this in 2 batches if necessary so the pieces will fit in a single layer without crowding the pan) and sauté over medium heat for 8-10 minutes until the chicken is golden brown on both sides (it won't be cooked through yet). Cover the casserole with a lid or foil and transfer to the oven. Bake for 45-60 minutes or until the chicken is tender and the flesh opaque all the way through.

Remove the chicken from the sauce and transfer to a plate. Add the apricots, cinnamon sticks and stock to the sauce in the casserole then bubble until reduced by a third to concentrate the flavour. Mix the cornflour to a smooth cream with a little stock or water then stir into the sauce and bubble until thickened.

Return the chicken and its juices to the casserole, bring back to a bubble, then sprinkle with the roasted nuts, parsley and pomegranate seeds. Bring to the table covered, so the lovely aromas are released when you remove the lid.

SYRIAN MEATBALLS

Serves: 6-8
Keeps: 3 days in the fridge
Freeze: 3 months
Per serving: 350 cals, 13 g carbs

Tender meatballs in a rich sweet-and-sour tomato sauce with warm spices and pine nuts.

Beef is a good source of B vitamins, iron, zinc, and selenium which may be cancer-protective, and high quality protein that can help prevent muscle loss in older people. If grass-fed, it can provide heart-healthy fatty acids.

Beef also contains saturated fat, however, so should be eaten in moderation, especially if you have high cholesterol (see page 250). Minced turkey or chicken thigh is a lower cholesterol alternative. Although minced poultry breast is lower still, it's too dry for good meatballs. For a gluten-free version, use GF oats and bread.

---

1 large red onion

handful of parsley

2 slices of wholemeal bread

2 eggs

1 tbsp dark soy sauce

1 tsp ground allspice
   or cinnamon

1 tsp fine sea salt

15 grinds black pepper

900 g (2 lb) beef
   or turkey thigh mince

For the sauce

1 medium red onion

2 tbsp extra virgin olive oil

50 g (2 oz) pine nuts

150 g (5 oz) tomato purée
   or 5 tbsp double concentrated
   tomato purée

300 ml (11 fl oz) water

juice of half a large lemon

1 tbsp honey

1 tsp fine sea salt

15 grinds black pepper

1 tbsp finely chopped
   flat-leaf parsley

Peel and roughly chop the onion and cut the coarse stalks off the parsley (save them for making stock.) Cut or tear the bread into small pieces. Put the parsley, eggs, onion, bread, soy sauce, and seasonings into a food processor or blender and process for 30 seconds. Transfer to a bowl, add the mince and mix with a large fork until evenly blended. Leave for 30 minutes to firm up.

To make the sauce, halve and peel the onion, then slice it as thinly as you can. Heat the oil in a 25-30 cm (10-12″) sauté pan or deep frying pan, add the onion and a pinch of salt, cover, and cook gently for 5-8 minutes until very soft. Add the pine nuts and cook stirring often, for 2-3 minutes until golden. Add all the remaining sauce ingredients except the parsley, and bring to a simmer, then check the seasoning.

Form the mincemeat mixture into balls the size of a golf ball and gently add them to the pan. They should be just covered with the sauce mixture – add a little water or stock if necessary.

Cover and simmer gently for 1 hour, either on the stove, or if more convenient, in a preheated oven at 170°C/Gas 3. With either method, uncover and bubble for a further 15 minutes to reduce the sauce and concentrate the flavour. Sprinkle with the parsley before serving.

STEALTHY MEATBALLS

Serves: 6
Keeps: 3 days in the fridge
Freeze: 3 months
Per serving: 250 cals, 11 g carbs

Even the most veggie-averse kids love these crispy little meatballs. The stealthy part is kale, a nutritional powerhouse, cunningly hidden in the mince mixture. If you don't want crispy meatballs, add them to the sauce without sautéing them beforehand and simmer, covered, for 30-40 minutes. For a gluten-free version, use gluten-free bread and oats.

white part of a leek
½ medium red onion
handful of shredded kale
handful of fresh parsley
1 slice wholegrain bread
1 egg
1 tsp fine sea salt
10 grinds black pepper
450 g (1 lb) beef or turkey
    thigh mince, or a mixture
4 tbsp rolled oats
2 tsp dark soy sauce
1-2 tbsp coconut oil

For the sauce
1 tbsp extra virgin olive oil
1 clove garlic
1 × 400 g tin chopped tomatoes
    or passata
2 tsp tomato purée
½ tsp herbes de Provence
    or dried basil
1 tsp honey
1 tsp sea salt
10 grinds black pepper
2 tsp lemon juice
2 sprigs flat-leaf parsley

Trim and thinly slice the leek, peel and roughly chop the onion. Process all the vegetables and parsley in a food processor until finely chopped then add the bread, torn into several pieces, and process until you have fine crumbs then pulse in the egg.

Put the mince, oats, seasonings, soy sauce, and the mixture from the food processor into a bowl and mix with a large fork until thoroughly blended. Leave for 30 minutes (and up to 2 hours) to firm up.

Roll the mixture into balls each about the size of a golf ball. Heat a tablespoon of coconut oil in your largest non-stick frying pan and swirl to coat with the oil. When hot, add just enough meatballs to fit comfortably in the pan without touching one another (about half.) They should sizzle when added to the pan. If not, turn up the heat (if the oil isn't hot enough the meatballs will fall apart.)

Cook the meatballs over medium-high heat without moving them for 3-4 minutes until nicely browned. Shake the pan to check they're not sticking then turn them gently and cook the second side for another 3-4 minutes (leave any that are stuck to continue cooking on the first side). Reduce the heat and continue to cook, jiggling the pan from time to time, until the meatballs are firm and a rich brown on all sides with no sign of pink in the centre.

Transfer them to a baking tray and cover loosely with foil, or pop them in the oven at 180°C/Gas 4 to keep warm. Cook the second batch as before, adding a little more oil to the pan if needed.

To make the sauce, add the olive oil and garlic crushed in a press, to the frying pan and cook over medium heat for 20 seconds until fragrant. Add all the remaining sauce ingredients, stirring well to incorporate any brown bits on the bottom of the pan. Cover and simmer for 8-10 minutes until thick and glossy. Remove the parsley sprigs and serve with the meatballs.

COTTAGE PIE WITH A TWIST

Serves: 6
Keeps: 2 days in the fridge
Freeze: 1 month
Per serving: 310 cals, 37 g carbs

Cottage pie is one of those dishes that have truly stood the test of time. Early Jewish immigrants from Eastern Europe were taught how to make it as part of their introduction to English life and culture.

We've upped its health credentials by using minced turkey instead of beef to reduce the cholesterol content, beefing up its flavour with umami-rich ingredients like dark soy and Worcestershire sauce, plus a little extra virgin olive oil to add richness. It's topped with a creamy mash of white and sweet potato for extra vitamin A and fibre. For a vegan version, use soy mince and add a teaspoon of yeast extract.

---

1 red onion

2 small carrots

2 sticks celery

2 tbsp olive oil

generous pinch salt

1 bay leaf

750 g turkey thigh mince

1 tbsp tomato purée

2 tbsp dark soy sauce or tamari

2 tbsp lower salt light soy sauce

1 tbsp extra virgin olive oil

2 tbsp wholemeal flour

90 ml (3 fl oz) bone broth
　or chicken stock

15 grinds black pepper

1 tbsp Worcestershire sauce

3 tbsp finely chopped flat-leaf
　parsley

For the topping

450 g (1 lb) sweet potatoes

450 g (1 lb) medium white
　potatoes (Maris Piper are ideal)

½ -1 tsp fine sea salt

5 grinds black pepper

generous pinch nutmeg

¼ tsp white pepper

50 ml (1½ fl oz) extra virgin
　olive oil

Peel, trim and finely chop the onion and carrots. Trim and finely chop the celery. Heat the oil in a medium sauté pan, add the onion and a pinch of salt, then cook over gentle heat, covered, for 6-8 minutes until soft and golden. Add the celery, bay leaf, mince, and soy sauces.

Cook uncovered over medium-high heat until the turkey is cooked through and most of the liquid has evaporated. Stir in the tomato purée and extra virgin olive oil, then gradually stir in the flour. Bubble for 2 minutes until the mixture has thickened, then add the stock, pepper and Worcestershire sauce. Transfer the mixture to an ovenproof casserole or gratin dish about 20 × 30 cm (8 × 12").

To make the topping, peel both types of potato and cut into 5 cm (2") chunks. Bring to the boil in a large pan of salted water, then cover and cook for 10-15 minutes or until a piece feels tender when pierced with a small pointed knife. Drain well, reserving the cooking liquid, then return them to the empty pan and shake over very gentle heat until the moisture has evaporated.

Add the seasonings, extra virgin olive oil and about 3 tablespoons of the reserved cooking liquid to the potatoes, then mash, or better still, whisk with a hand-held electric beater until smooth and fluffy. Check the seasoning, adding more salt, pepper or nutmeg if it tastes a little bland, and more liquid if very thick. Spread the mash over the mince mixture and fork into a design. Bake for 30 minutes at 180°C/Gas 4 until bubbling and golden brown. If necessary, pop it under the grill for the last 3-5 minutes to brown the top.

JUDI'S TIP: most recipes that call for minced beef or lamb work really well with turkey thigh mince mixed with a tablespoon of dark soy sauce and a teaspoon of olive oil before cooking.

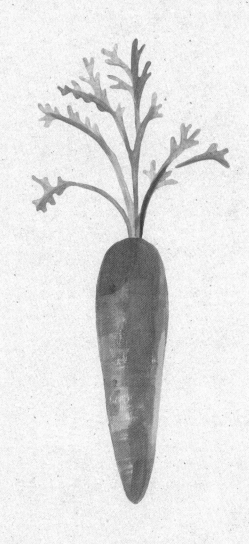

7 | SIDES

MARINATED GRILLED VEGETABLES WITH GARLIC & HERBS

Serves: 8

Keeps: 1-2 days in the fridge

Do not freeze

Per serving: 120 cals, 14 g carbs

An exuberant rainbow of tender vegetables that makes a lovely summer side dish and can be made well ahead. The veggies can be cooked on a barbecue or indoors on the stove in a heavy, ridged grill pan (cast iron is ideal).

With its colourful assortment of vegetables and a garlic and herb dressing, this platter really packs a punch of vitamins, minerals, prebiotics, and antioxidants. Feel free to improvise your own favourite vegetables, but root vegetables will need to be steamed or microwaved until tender before grilling.

---

2 courgettes

6 baby or 2 medium
aubergines

6 shallots or 2 small red onions

8 baby mixed colour peppers,
or 1 each large red, orange
and yellow pepper

10-12 cherry
or grape tomatoes

1 bunch asparagus

handful steamed or boiled
baby carrots

olive oil

For the marinade

2 tbsp extra virgin olive oil

juice of 1 lemon

2 cloves garlic

3 sprigs flat-leaved parsley

4 sprigs fresh thyme

½ tsp fine sea salt

10 grinds black pepper

To serve

sprigs of fresh parsley, thyme
or basil

Cut the trimmed courgettes on the diagonal into long 1 cm (½") thick slices, and the aubergines lengthways into 1 cm (½") slices. Halve the shallots or onions, peel and cut into wedges. If using large peppers, remove the pith and seeds then cut into 6 strips (leave baby peppers whole).

Put all the vegetables in a large bowl (or several smaller ones), sprinkle lightly with salt then drizzle with the olive oil and toss to coat thoroughly.

Heat an outdoor barbecue, or a ridged grill pan on the stove, until very hot. Brush lightly with oil using a silicone brush, then cook the vegetables in batches by type. Don't move or turn them for the first few minutes so they take on grill marks, then turn them over with tongs and cook the second side.

Allow 3-5 minutes in total for asparagus, 2-3 minutes for tomatoes, 10 minutes for peppers, and 6-8 minutes for courgettes, aubergines, onions, and mushrooms. If the veggies stick, brush the pan with a bit more oil. Transfer the cooked vegetables to a bowl or large container.

Peel and crush the garlic through a press. Remove the coarse stalks from the herbs and finely chop the leaves. Put all the marinade ingredients into a screw-top jar and shake well then pour over the warm vegetables. Leave to marinate at room temperature for 1-5 hours, or overnight in the fridge (remove from the fridge at least 2 hours before serving to come to room temperature).

Arrange the vegetables on a large platter (they can be left covered with clingfilm for several hours at room temperature). Before serving, sprinkle lightly with sea salt and black pepper and garnish with sprigs of herbs.

PETITS POIS AUX POIREAUX BRAISED PEAS & LEEKS

Serves: 6
Keeps: 2 days in the fridge
Freeze: 1 month
Per serving: 90 cals, 8 g carbs

A quick way to "dress up" peas. Leeks contain inulin, a type of fibre that's good for gastrointestinal health, can help lower cholesterol and regulate blood sugar. Petits pois are naturally sweet, high in fibre, and vitamins A, B, C, and K.

1 slender leek
30 g (1 oz) butter
450 g (1 lb) frozen petits pois or garden peas
½ tsp salt
10 grinds black pepper

Trim and thinly slice the white part of the leek. Melt the butter in a deep sauté pan and add the leek, cover, and braise gently until soft, about 5 minutes. Add the peas, salt, and pepper, then cook until the peas are tender. The dish can now be left for several hours covered with clingfilm. Reheat gently on the stove, or transfer to a serving dish and microwave until hot.

GOLDEN SPICE-ROASTED CAULIFLOWER

Serves: 6
Keeps: 2 days in the fridge
Do not freeze
Per serving: 84 cals, 9 g carbs

A colourful Indian-inspired addition to any meal. Roasting really brings out the best in cauliflower and preserves far more of its nutrients than boiling. Cauliflower and mustard seeds contain compounds that may help prevent cancer.

1 large cauliflower
3 spring onions
2 tbsp olive oil
1 tbsp water
¼ tsp cayenne or hot paprika
1 tsp turmeric
2 tsp cumin seeds
1 tsp fennel seeds
1 tsp mustard seeds
½ tsp fine sea salt

Preheat the oven to 200°C/Gas 6 and line a large baking tray or roasting tin with foil for easy cleaning up. Remove the stalk and coarse outer leaves from the cauliflower but keep any pale green inner leaves. Separate the head into bite-sized florets then rinse and drain. Cut the trimmed spring onions into 2 cm (¾") pieces.

Put the oil, water, spices and seasonings in a roasting tin, add the cauliflower and toss so everything is nicely coated. Roast for 15 minutes, then flip the cauliflower pieces over with a spatula and roast for another 10-15 minutes until tender and tinged with brown. Reheats well in the microwave or in the oven covered with foil at 180°C-200°C/Gas 4-6.

> Pictured overleaf

CITRUS GLAZED CARROTS

Serves: 4-6
Keeps: 1 day in the fridge
Do not freeze
Per serving: 68 cals, 12 g carbs

Sweet yet tangy, this is a wonderful way to cook carrots. They can be prepared earlier in the day and reheated on the stove or transferred to a serving dish and microwaved at the last minute. For a vegan version, use extra virgin olive oil instead of butter.

450 g (1 lb) young carrots
1 lime
1 tsp ground coriander
600 ml (1 pint) vegetable stock or water
juice of a small orange
1 tbsp butter

Peel the carrots and cut them into 5 mm (¼") diagonal slices. Cut a long strip of zest from the lime with a vegetable peeler, then finely grate the rest of the zest.

Put the peel and all the other ingredients except the grated zest and orange juice into a sauté pan or large frying pan and simmer, uncovered, for 15-20 minutes or until the carrots are bite-tender when pierced with a sharp knife. Add the orange juice and bubble for 5 minutes or until most of the liquid has evaporated and the carrots are coated with a shiny glaze. Before serving, remove the strip of peel and sprinkle with the grated zest.

SPICED SWEET POTATO WEDGES

Serves: 6-8
Eat freshly roasted
Per serving: 128 cals, 25 g carbs

Crisp on the outside, tender inside, these are a healthy alternative to regular roast potatoes. Sweet potatoes contain more fibre and have a lower glycaemic index than white potatoes. They're also rich in vitamin A for healthy eyes.

6-8 small orange or purple sweet potatoes
½ tsp fine sea salt
10 grinds black pepper
2 tbsp olive oil
2 tsp paprika
½ tsp dried thyme or oregano
¼ tsp cayenne or hot paprika

Preheat the oven to 200°C/Gas 6 and line a large roasting tin or baking tray with foil. Scrub the potatoes but don't peel them, then rinse, drain well and cut each potato into 6 wedges. Add the oil and potatoes to the tin, sprinkle with the seasonings and toss to coat with the spiced oil, then spread the wedges in a single layer.

Roast for 15 minutes until brown on the underside, then turn them over with tongs or a spatula and roast for a further 10 minutes to brown the other side. Transfer to a warm serving dish – they'll continue to crispen as they cool.

> Pictured overleaf

TURKISH GREEN BEANS

Serves: 6
Keeps: 2 days in the fridge
Freeze: 1 month
Per serving: 82 cals, 13 g carbs

This is particularly good made with stringless runner beans, but regular or fine green beans work well too. In the traditional version, the beans are braised for nearly an hour, rendering them soft and yellowish. Instead, we blanch them briefly to preserve the nutrients and their vivid emerald colour.

450 g (1 lb) fresh or frozen green beans
1 tsp salt
1-2 tbsp extra virgin olive oil
3 shallots or a small onion
½ tsp fine sea salt
3 medium cloves garlic
400 g tin chopped tomatoes
juice of a small orange
10 grinds black pepper

Bring a large pan of water to the boil. Trim the fresh beans, removing the strings if necessary. If using runner beans, cut them in half or into diagonal pieces. Add the salt and fresh beans to the boiling water and bubble for 3-5 minutes – the beans should still be bite-crisp – then drain, drench immediately with very cold water to set the colour. When cold, drain well.

Peel and finely chop the shallots or onion. Heat the oil in a large, non-stick sauté pan, add the shallots or onion, sprinkle with the sea salt, and cook gently for 5 minutes until soft and golden. Add the garlic, tomatoes, orange juice, and seasonings. Simmer for 10-15 minutes until thickened but still juicy.

Now add the drained fresh or the frozen beans, simmer for 5 minutes or until bite tender, then leave to cool in the sauce so the flavours can mingle. Serve warm or at room temperature. The dish reheats well, but don't cover it if you want the beans to stay bright green.

> Pictured on previous page

QUICK ROASTED VEGETABLES
WITH FENNEL & GINGER

Serves: 6
Keeps: 1 day in the fridge
Do not freeze
Per serving: 75 cals, 14 g carbs

Roasting vegetables that are usually boiled or steamed can be a revelation. The dish can be assembled several hours ahead, ready to pop in the oven and roast half an hour or so before serving.

Fennel can prevent abdominal colicky pain, onions and asparagus are good for your gut, while sprouts are thought to have cancer-protective properties.

450 g (1 lb) young carrots
a handful of peeled shallots or pearl onions
1 small bulb fennel
handful of Brussels sprouts
100 g (3 ½ oz) fresh asparagus
1-2 tbsp olive oil
2 cloves garlic
½ tsp fine sea salt
2 tsp grated fresh ginger

Trim the carrots (no need to peel if they're young) and cut any that are particularly thick in half lengthwise. Trim, halve and peel the shallots. Top and tail the fennel and cut into 4-6 wedges. Trim and halve the sprouts (except for any that are really small).

Put the oil in a gratin dish or non-stick roasting tin large enough to hold the vegetables in one layer. Add the vegetables and the unpeeled garlic, sprinkle with the salt, and mix to coat with the seasoned oil.

Preheat the oven to 200°C/Gas 6. Roast the vegetables for 10 minutes then add the grated ginger and mix gently so they're well coated. Roast for a further 15-20 minutes or until tender and tinged with brown. Just before serving, mix gently.

JUDI'S TIPS: thick asparagus, especially if it's white, should be peeled or snapped off near the base to remove the tough woody part, then halved lengthwise before roasting. Large, mature carrots need to be peeled and cut into batons about the size and thickness of young carrots. Or use a pack of ready-to-eat mini-carrots which need no preparation.

A MEDLEY OF SPRING VEGETABLES

Serves: 4-6
Keeps: 1 day in the fridge
Do not freeze
Per serving: 110 cals, 13 g carbs

The beauty of this dish comes from the variety of colours and textures, and a wide assortment of vegetables ensures a great mix of phytonutrients. The veggies can be blanched several hours ahead then finished with the sauce and herbs before serving.

---

200 g (7 oz) new potatoes

200 g (7 oz) baby carrots

100 g (3½ oz) baby turnips
or swedes

small bunch of radishes

200 g (7 oz) fresh asparagus

150 g (5 oz) sugar snap peas
or mange tout

handful of fresh or frozen
~~butter~~ beans or peas
BROAD

For the lemon butter

40 g (1½ oz) butter

1 tbsp freshly squeezed
lemon juice

½ tsp salt

5 grinds black pepper

1 tbsp fresh snipped chives

2 tsp finely chopped
flat-leaf parsley

Cut the potatoes into quarters lengthwise, or in half if very small. Leave tiny carrots whole, or cut larger ones into 5 cm (2") pieces. Peel and cut the baby turnips or swedes into slim wedges. Trim the radishes, top and tail the sugar snap peas, and snap off the tough lower stalks of the asparagus.

Bring a large pan of water to the boil and add 2 teaspoons of salt. Add the potatoes and turnips or swedes, boil for 5 minutes then add the carrots. Simmer until bite-tender, about 10 minutes, then remove them with a slotted spoon and transfer to a bowl.

Fill a large bowl with chilled water, and place a colander in the sink. Bring the cooking water back to the boil and add the remaining vegetables. Boil for 3-5 minutes or until bite tender, then drain in the colander and drench under cold running water for 2-3 minutes until cool. Transfer to the bowl of chilled water to set the colour, then drain.

Melt the butter in a large sauté pan. Add the potatoes, carrots, and turnips or swedes, and heat gently for 2 minutes. Add the remaining vegetables, toss to coat them with the butter and cook gently until heated through. Add the lemon juice, salt, pepper, and herbs, mix gently and serve.

ALSACE LENTILS
WITH WHITE WINE & LEEKS

Serves: 4
Keeps: 3 days in the fridge
Freeze: 2 months
Per serving: 280 cals, 34 g carbs

Puy or French green lentils (lentilles vertes) hold their shape when cooked, giving a lovely texture to this warming classic from Alsace – where bagels and chopped liver are said to have been invented. The combination of the nutty lentils and vegetables is irresistible.

Serve the lentils as a bed for roast chicken, duck, or salmon, or as a vegetarian meal in itself. Dried lentils give the best texture and flavour, although packs of ready-to-eat Puy lentils may be easier to come by. For a vegan version, or if serving with meat, use 2 teaspoons extra virgin olive oil instead of butter.

---

1 medium onion

1 large carrot

white part of 1 medium leek

1 medium stalk of celery

30 g (1 oz) butter

1 tsp extra virgin olive oil

1 bay leaf

175 g (6 oz) French green lentils

750 ml (1¼ pints) vegetable stock

225 ml (8 fl oz) dry
  but fruity white wine

½ tsp salt

15 grinds black pepper

Peel, trim and chop all the vegetables as finely as you can, either by hand or food processor. Rinse the lentils and drain.

Heat the butter and oil in a medium saucepan. Add the vegetables, bay leaf and a pinch of the salt then cook gently, covered, for 10 minutes or until soft and golden.

Add the lentils, stock, and wine. Bring to the boil then reduce the heat, and simmer very gently for 40-50 minutes or until the lentils are tender but still hold their shape. Remove the bay leaf and stir in the black pepper. Serve warm or at room temperature.

TO USE PRE-COOKED LENTILS:

Use a 350 g pack of ready-to-eat Puy lentils. Cook the vegetables in the butter and oil for 5 minutes as before, then add just enough stock or water to cover them.

Simmer with the lid on for 10 minutes then add the lentils, salt, pepper and 100 ml each of wine and stock. Simmer for 5 minutes then leave to sit, covered, for the lentils to absorb the flavours. Serve warm or at room temperature.

LEGUMES such as beans, peas, lentils and chickpeas, are rich in B vitamins that help prevent dementia. High in protein, rich in iron, and inexpensive, they're a must-have in any kitchen store-cupboard, be it frozen, dried or tinned (without added sugar). Thanks to their high fibre content, legumes can help reduce the risk of diabetes, lower LDL cholesterol, and help prevent cancer.

MUJADARRA

LEBANESE LENTILS WITH CARAMELISED ONIONS

Serves: 8-10
Keeps: 3 days in the fridge
Freeze: 3 months
Per serving: 170 cals, 30 g carbs

A mouthwatering combination of crispy caramelised onions, nutty bulgur and lentils, this is a Middle Eastern classic. It's topped with a dollop of cool, creamy yoghurt sauce laced with fresh mint and finished with dukkah, a crunchy roasted nut and spice mix.

If you prefer, use quick-cooking bulgur and 2 packs of ready to eat Puy lentils, but don't skip the caramelised onions that we think really make the dish.

Bulgur and lentils help regulate blood sugar and cholesterol. Lentils also provide protein and folic acid to help lower the risk of Alzheimer's and heart disease. Dukkah contains sesame seeds so don't serve to someone who is allergic to sesame.

---

200 g (7 oz) Puy, French green, or brown lentils

350 ml (12 fl oz) strong vegetable stock

200 g (7 oz) coarse bulgur

20 grinds black pepper

3 medium onions

For the spiced yoghurt

2 tbsp chopped fresh mint

100-150 g (4-5 oz) Greek yoghurt

1 tsp fresh lemon juice

generous pinch fine sea salt

10 grinds black pepper

pinch Aleppo pepper, hot paprika, or cayenne

To serve

2 tbsp chopped flat-leaf parsley

1 tbsp Dukkah (page 67), or 1 tbsp cumin seeds, toasted in a frying pan for 2-3 minutes until fragrant

Rinse and drain the dried lentils. Bring the stock to the boil in a sauté pan or saucepan, add the lentils, and ½ a teaspoon of salt. Simmer, covered, for 20-25 minutes, or until the lentils are just tender. Add the bulgur, re-cover, and simmer until all the liquid has been absorbed and the bulgur is al dente, 10-15 minutes (if you're using ready to eat lentils, add them now). Leave to rest with the lid on for 5 minutes then fluff up the grains with a fork.

Meanwhile, peel and slice the onions thinly. Heat the oil in a large sauté pan, add the onions sprinkled with ½ a teaspoon of sea salt, then cover and cook over medium heat for 10 minutes, stirring occasionally, until the onions are very soft and golden. Uncover and cook for another 10-15 minutes, stirring often, until the onions are richly browned. If they start to stick or burn add a tablespoon of water. Increase the heat and cook the onions for another few minutes without stirring so the bottom layer can crispen slightly.

To make the spiced yoghurt sauce, mix the chopped mint with the yoghurt, lemon juice, seasonings, and spices. Transfer to a small bowl, cover and chill.

Have ready a warm serving dish. Turn the bulgur and lentils into the dish, stir in the black pepper and up to ½ teaspoon of salt, then top with the caramelised onions and chopped parsley. Top each serving with a spoonful of the spiced yoghurt sprinkled with dukkah or cumin.

STIR-FRIED SEASONAL GREENS

Serves: 6
Keeps: 1 day in the fridge
after cooking
Per serving: 102 cals, 8 g carbs

Quick and tasty, this makes a great side for fish, chicken, or as part of a vegan meal with rice or quinoa. Our favourite greens are sprouting or long-stemmed broccoli, baby asparagus and pak choi, but feel free to improvise with similar tender green veggies.

Pak choi and broccoli, both cruciferous, are a good source of glucosinolates and selenium, which help protect against cancer, and folate for bone and heart health. Omit the sesame oil if anyone is allergic.

450 g pak choi or choi sum
450 g (1 lb) broccoli
small bunch of fresh asparagus
2.5 cm (1") piece of fresh ginger
150 g (5 oz) trimmed
  sugar snap peas
  or mangetout
2 peeled garlic cloves
2 tbsp coconut or rapeseed oil
½ tsp fine sea salt
2 tbsp stock or water
1 tsp light soy sauce
1-2 tsp unrefined sesame oil

Prepare all the vegetables beforehand. Cut the pak choi into 7 cm (3") pieces, separating the white stalks from the green leaves. Peel the coarse skin from the broccoli stem with a vegetable peeler, then thinly slice the pale green stem and break the broccoli head into florets.

Snap off the coarse lower stalks of the asparagus, discard them (or save for stock), then cut the spears into bite-sized pieces. Peel and thinly slice the ginger, then stack up the slices and cut them into very thin slivers – in Chinese cooking, these are called "silken threads". Peel and thinly slice the garlic.

Heat an empty wok or large heavy frying pan over high heat for a minute, then add the oil and a pinch of salt to the oil. Add the ginger, garlic, and vegetables, except the pak choi leaves. Stir-fry over high heat for 2-3 minutes, then reduce the heat and add the stock and soy sauce. Cover and bubble for 2-3 minutes or until the vegetables are bite tender then uncover, add the pak choi leaves and sprinkle with the sesame oil. If necessary, the vegetables may be reheated for 2-3 minutes before serving.

OIL for stir-frying needs a high smoke point so it doesn't break down into harmful compounds at the temperatures needed to stir-fry successfully. Coconut and rapeseed oil are the healthiest options. Butter and extra virgin olive oil are not suitable for stir-frying, nor is toasted sesame oil, which should only be added at the end of cooking.

8 | DESSERTS

MIRKATAN ARMENIAN FRUIT COMPOTE

Serves: 6-8
Keeps: 1 week in the fridge
Per serving: 235 cals, 37 g carbs

This ancient dish of plump and juicy dried fruits mixed with walnuts and fresh oranges in a light cinnamon syrup was traditionally served as a pick-me-up to weary visitors. We love it after a meal topped with a spoonful of cool, rosewater-scented yoghurt.

Tea, especially green tea, is a great source of antioxidants. For mirkatan, we like to use chai, Earl Grey or hibiscus tea to plump up the fruit, but any sort of tea will do. Dried fruits are high in fibre and boron, good for digestive health and helping prevent osteoporosis.

225 g (8 oz) each pitted prunes, dried apricots, and dried peaches, apples or pears, 680 g (1½ lb) in total
125 g (4 oz) raisins or sultanas
small pot of freshly brewed tea
75 g (3 oz) walnut halves
150 ml (5 fl oz) dry red wine, or low sugar red grape juice
3 strips of orange peel
2 cinnamon sticks
1 tbsp fresh lemon juice

To serve
4-5 tbsp Greek yoghurt
2-3 drops of rosewater
1 tbsp chopped pistachios

The day before, put the dried fruit in a bowl and pour the strained tea over it. Cover and leave overnight.

The next day, strain the fruit into a bowl, reserving the liquid, and insert a walnut half into each prune – this helps the prunes hold their shape after poaching.

Make up the reserved tea with water if needed, so you have 225 ml (8 fl oz) of liquid. Put the tea in a wide pan with the wine or juice, orange peel, and cinnamon sticks. Bring to the boil and simmer uncovered for 3 minutes.

Add the dried fruit, cover, and simmer for 20 minutes until the fruit is tender and the syrup has thickened slightly. Stir in the lemon juice.

Remove the strip of orange peel before serving the mirkatan warm or at room temperature with the Greek yoghurt flavoured with rosewater and sprinkled with pistachios.

PEACHES AND APRICOTS are rich in vitamin A that can help protect you against heart disease, and may also help reduce your risk of cancer. Like nectarines, they're a good source of potassium, which can help lower your blood pressure, as well as vitamins C and B3 that may reduce LDL cholesterol and help prevent depression.

POMEGRANATE ROSE GRANITA

Serves: 6-8
Freeze: 1 month
Per serving: 48 cals, 12 g carbs

When Israeli pomegranates are in season, piles of fruit abound on every street corner in Jerusalem, with vendors hawking cups of freshly pressed ruby juice on demand.

Now that pure pomegranate juice is widely available in bottles, this refreshing granita, subtly perfumed with rosewater, makes a wonderful palate cleanser to serve after a main course and before dessert and is a cinch to make.

If you have a food mill, it's easy to extract the juice from fresh pomegranates. If you can only find pomegranate juice drink, which contains added sugar, omit the sugar in the recipe.

---

500 ml (17 fl oz) fresh or bottled pure pomegranate juice

2 tsp sugar

1 tbsp freshly squeezed lemon juice

1 tsp rosewater

fresh pomegranate seeds

Simmer the pomegranate juice in a saucepan for 8-10 minutes to intensify its flavour. Stir in the sugar, leave to cool, then add the lemon juice and rose water. Pour into a shallow container and freeze for 2 hours.

Using a large fork, scrape the frozen mixture across the surface and sides – it should look like coarse snow. Freeze for another 2 hours then repeat the scraping process until all the mixture is like coarse pink snow. The granita can now be frozen in an airtight container for up to a week.

Serve in very small glass dishes sprinkled with pomegranate seeds.

POMEGRANATES are a great source of a powerful antioxidant called punicalagin, and punicic acid, which is anti-inflammatory and may help reduce cancer. Pomegranates are also good for heart and brain health.

GRILLED SUMMER FRUIT
WITH STRAWBERRY SAUCE

Serves: 6-8
Keeps: 3 days in the fridge
Per serving: 96 cals, 21 g carbs

Searing fresh seasonal fruit on a griddle or BBQ brings out its sweetness and flavour. Plums, nectarines, apricots and pineapple all work beautifully on the grill, as do some less obvious candidates such as strawberries, mango and watermelon.

4 white or yellow nectarines

6 pink or yellow apricots

6 plums

1 large punnet strawberries

2 tsp coconut oil

1 tsp caster sugar or erythritol

squeeze of fresh lemon
  or lime juice

sprigs of fresh mint
  or lemon verbena

Heat a ridged cast iron grill pan or barbecue grill for 10 minutes until extremely hot. Meanwhile, halve and pit the stone fruit and hull the strawberries.

Using a silicone brush (or a wad of paper towel held in kitchen tongs and dipped in the oil) lightly oil the surface of the pan or grill. Add the strawberries, cook for 2 minutes, then transfer to a dish.

Add as much stone fruit, cut side up, to the hot grill as will fit in a single layer. Cook the fruit for 3 minutes without moving it around the pan so it takes on grill marks, then carefully turn each piece over with a spatula or tongs and cook the second side. If the fruit sticks to the pan, add a little more oil. Transfer to a warm platter then cook the rest in the same way, brushing the grill with oil again if necessary.

To make the sauce, purée half of the grilled strawberries with the lemon juice and sugar in a food processor or blender then transfer to a small bowl. Add the remaining strawberries to the platter and decorate with the sprigs of mint or lemon verbena. Serve warm or at room temperature.

STRAWBERRIES are a delicious way to boost your iodine levels, important for your thyroid and metabolism, and, during pregnancy for the baby's brain health. Like all berries, strawberries help regulate your blood sugar and can reduce the risk of diabetes. If you do suffer from diabetes, eating berries is a healthy way to satisfy a craving for something sweet.

MARRAKESH ORANGES
WITH ORANGE BLOSSOM & CINNAMON

Serves: 6-8
Keeps: 2 days in the fridge
Freeze: 3 months
Per serving: 65 cals, 17 g carbs

Simple but refreshing, and particularly striking made with blood oranges if in season. For a special meal, serve it with Pomegranate Granita (page 178) and Featherlight Lemon Kichlach (page 204).

6-8 medium oranges

1 tsp orange blossom
   or rose water

1 tsp ground cinnamon

tiny sprigs or leaves of fresh mint,
   lemon-scented geranium,
   or lemon verbena

Cut a thin slice off the top and bottom of the oranges (this makes them easier to peel) then cut off the peel and pith. Remove any remaining pith with a small sharp knife.

Cut each orange into 6-8 slices and arrange on a serving platter then sprinkle with the orange blossom or rose water.

If not serving immediately, cover tightly with clingfilm and leave for up to 3 hours at room temperature, or up to 24 in the fridge.

Just before serving, dust with cinnamon and decorate with the sprigs of mint, geranium or lemon verbena.

ORANGES like all citrus fruit, produce hesperidin, a chemical which helps to improve circulation, and the antioxidant, quercetin, which may reduce the risk of diabetes, asthma and heart disease. They also contain very high levels of vitamin C that helps the body fight against infection.

FRESH PEACH CROSTATA

Serves: 6-8
Keeps: 2 days in the fridge
Freeze: 3 months
Per serving: 262 cals, 31 g carbs

A crostata is an Italian free-form rustic tart with a tender, buttery crust folded over a juicy fruit filling. It's easy to make and looks gorgeous. We use some spelt flour in the crust (plain wholemeal works too) to add fibre but without compromising its melt in-the-mouth texture.

For the pastry
1 egg
2 tsp lemon juice
1-2 tbsp cold water
125 g (4 oz) cold butter
85 g (3 oz) spelt flour
140 g (5 oz) plain flour
2 tsp caster sugar

For the filling
4 ripe peaches or nectarines
1 tbsp spelt flour
1 tbsp freshly squeezed
   orange juice
1 tsp soft brown sugar
squeeze of lemon juice

To glaze
1-2 tsp low-sugar
   apricot conserve
squeeze of lemon juice

Separate the egg. Reserve the white for glazing the pastry, and whisk the yolk, water and lemon juice together. Cut the cold butter into small cubes, then put the flour, sugar and butter into a food processor and pulse until it resembles fine crumbs. Add the yolk mixture through the feed-tube and process until it looks like a moist crumble, about 10 seconds.

Turn onto a lightly floured surface and knead gently with your fingertips to remove any cracks. Flatten into a disk, wrap in clingfilm or foil and chill for 20 minutes and up to 24 hours, or freeze until needed.

Preheat the oven to 200°C/Gas 6. Cut the unpeeled fruit into 2 cm (¾") slices – if the stone clings to the flesh, just cut around it so you have 4 large pieces of fruit, then into slices. Mix the fruit with the rest of the filling ingredients.

Lay the chilled pastry on a large sheet of baking paper, cover with a large sheet of clingfilm and roll out into a 30 cm (12") disc – this stops it sticking to the rolling pin without having to use extra flour. Peel off the clingfilm – if the pastry has become too soft and sticky to separate from the clingfilm, pop it into the freezer for 5-10 minutes, then try again.

Pile the fruit in the centre of the pastry, leaving a 4 cm (1½") margin clear of fruit around the circumference. Bring the pastry margin in, pleating it to create a circular enclosure that leaves most of the filling exposed. Using the side of your hand, coax the outer edge of the crostata into a neat circle.

Whisk the egg white until frothy then brush it over the exposed pastry. Bake for 20 minutes, then reduce the heat to 190°C/Gas 5 and bake for a further 15 minutes or until the pastry is a rich golden brown.

Transfer the crostata to a cooling rack, leave for 5 minutes then slide the paper out from underneath – this stops the underside becoming soggy. Warm the apricot conserve with the lemon juice until liquidy, then lightly glaze the pastry and exposed fruit using a silicone brush.

LOKSHEN KUGEL WITH FOREST FRUITS

Serves: 6-8
Keeps: 3 days in the fridge
Freeze: 3 months
Per serving: 162 cals, 42 g carbs

Wild berries and orchard fruits abound in the forests and villages of Eastern Europe, and this kugel, studded with juicy cherries, plums, and berries perfumed with citrus and cinnamon, is a throwback to the version our great-grandmothers might have made.

We like to use spelt noodles which are higher in protein and lower in refined starch than egg noodles, and to rely mostly on the natural sugars in the fruit for sweetness.

To make it ahead, chill the baked kugel in the tin or dish. Shortly before serving, reheat, covered, at 180°C/Gas 4, or in the microwave until warmed through.

Berries contain ellagic acid, a phytochemical that may have cancer-protective properties, and cherries help reduce inflammation.

---

225 g (8 oz) frozen forest fruits
    or a mix of frozen dark sweet
    pitted cherries and berries

2-3 tbsp coconut oil

4 ripe plums

2 Braeburn or Cox's apples,
    or other flavourful eating apples

1 large egg

grated zest and juice of a small
    orange or tangerine

120 g (4 oz) sultanas, raisins
    or mixed dried fruit

1 tsp vanilla extract

1 tsp cinnamon

225 g (8 oz) medium wide spelt
    noodles or tagliatelle

Defrost the frozen fruit and drain well (keep the juice for smoothies). Set the oven to 180°C/Gas 4. Put the fat into an ovenproof dish or a 20 cm (8") cake tin at least 8 cm (3") deep, and place in the oven to melt as the oven heats up.

Put the lightly beaten egg, citrus zest and juice, dried fruit, vanilla, and cinnamon in a bowl. Pit and roughly chop the plums, coarsely grate the unpeeled apples as far as the core, then add to the egg mixture.

Cook the noodles in boiling water until barely tender, 3-4 minutes for spelt noodles, 8-10 minutes for egg tagliatelle. Drain then immediately add to the apple mixture, mixing well with a large fork. Add the berries and mix gently.

Swirl the hot melted fat around the baking dish or tin then add the noodle mixture – it may sizzle. Bake for 35-45 minutes at 180°C/Gas 4 until the kugel is set and golden brown. Let it rest for 10-15 minutes before cutting into wedges or squares. Serve warm.

JUDI'S TIPS: if for some reason you overcook your kugel and it gets a bit dry, whizz up a quick sauce with some berries and a little fresh orange or tangerine juice to serve with it. If you need the oven on at a lower temperature for something else, you can also bake your kugel at 150°C/Gas 2 for 1½ hours.

QUICK PLUM KUCHEN

Serves: 8-10
Keeps: 2 days in the fridge
Freeze: 1 month
Per serving: 197 cals, 22 g carbs

An old recipe from Vienna, this moist sponge cake studded with juicy plums is equally good as an after-dinner dessert or with a cup of coffee or tea. The butter must be very soft – the consistency of soft margarine. Almond extract and a sprinkling of nuts add a delicious touch, but can be omitted if someone is allergic.

For the cake batter

125 g (4 oz) self-raising flour
1 tsp baking powder
125 g (4 oz) very soft butter
2 large eggs
50 g (2 oz) caster sugar
Finely grated zest of a lemon
½ tsp almond extract
  or 1 tsp vanilla extract

For the topping

900 g (2 lb) ripe plums
1 tsp vanilla extract
squeeze of fresh lemon juice
1 tsp cinnamon mixed with
  1 tsp caster sugar
2 tbsp flaked almonds

Preheat the oven to 180°C/Gas 4. Lightly oil the inside of a 22 cm (9") flan dish, or oil then line the bottom and sides of a 20 cm (8") springform or loose-bottomed cake tin.

Put all the batter ingredients in a food processor and process for 10 seconds. Take off the lid, scrape down the sides of the bowl with a rubber spatula, then replace the lid and process for a further five seconds until smooth.

Alternatively, beat until smooth in a stand mixer or by hand in a bowl.

Turn the batter into the prepared dish or tin and smooth level. Halve and pit the plums then toss with the lemon juice and vanilla extract. Arrange them neatly over the batter then sprinkle with the cinnamon sugar and flaked almonds.

Bake for 35-40 minutes or until the cake is golden brown and firm to the touch and a skewer comes out clean from the centre.

Serve warm or at room temperature, plain or with Greek yoghurt.

PLUMS are packed with anthocyanins which help protect against cancer and cell damage. They're also great for relieving digestive problems. A medium fresh plum contains 113 mg of potassium, which helps manage high blood pressure and may reduce your risk of suffering a stroke.

APPLE & LEMON CRISP WITH MIXED BERRIES

Serves: 6 -8
Keeps: 3 days in the fridge
Freeze: 3 months
Per serving: 390 cals, 54 g carbs

The crunchy streusel topping atop a compote of lightly cooked fruit, is gluten-free and high in fibre. Brown rice flour has been milled for centuries, and can be used for a host of gluten-free dishes from biscuits to baby food.

Berries are high in anthocyanins to give your body's antioxidant defences a boost, and the apples rich in pectin fibre and quercetin which can help protect against heart disease, cancer and asthma. Nuts contain protein, monounsaturated fat and vitamin E, but if you're allergic, use an additional 2 tablespoons of oats, plus 2 tablespoons of gluten-free oat bran or ground flaxseeds, and an extra tablespoon of sunflower seeds for the topping in place of the ground and chopped nuts.

For the filling

225 g (8 oz) fresh or frozen
    mixed berries or fruits
    of the forest

6 Braeburn or Cox's apples

½ an unwaxed lemon

2-3 tbsp sultanas or raisins

juice and finely grated zest
    of 1 orange

For the streusel topping

85 g (3 oz) brown rice flour,
    or gluten-free plain flour

85 g (3 oz) ground almonds
    or hazelnuts

1 tsp ground ginger

1 tsp cinnamon

30 g (1 oz) gluten-free oats

55 g (2 oz) muscovado sugar

55 g (2 oz) very soft butter
    or coconut oil

1 tbsp sunflower seeds

3 tbsp roughly chopped
    hazelnuts, pecans, or walnuts

Defrost and drain the berries in a sieve (save any juice that comes out for smoothies). Preheat the oven to 200°C/Gas 6 and have ready a baking dish about 25 × 20× 4 cm (10 × 8 × 1½").

Peel, core and cut the apples into ½ cm (¼") slices. Arrange the apples in an even layer in the baking dish and scatter with the berries. Cut the unpeeled lemon into very thin slices then into quarters and add to the fruit with the sultanas, orange zest and juice.

To make the streusel topping, mix the rice flour, ground almonds, spices and sugar in a bowl or food processor. Rub in the fat by hand or pulse in a food processor until moist and crumbly. Stir in the oats and chopped nuts and sprinkle in an even layer over the apples.

Bake for 30 minutes or until the apples feel tender when pierced with a slim pointed knife and the topping is golden brown and crisp. Serve warm, either plain or with Greek yoghurt.

JUDI'S TIP: in season, fresh peaches, plums, or nectarines can be used instead of apples. Cooking apples work too, but are less sweet than eating apples, so you may find you need to add a little honey or fresh orange juice.

A STRUDEL OF PURPLE FRUITS

Serves: 6-8
Keeps: filling only: 3 days
in the fridge
Freeze: unbaked strudel 1 month
Per serving: 260 cals, 50 g carbs

As delicious as it is dramatic, this superb strudel filled with cherries and plums is a winner on the healthy eating front too. With no added sugar, its sweetness comes from the fruit. Toasted nuts and brown breadcrumbs absorb any liquid from the fruit to help keep the delicate pastry crisp. The filling must be cold or it will make the pastry soggy, so prepare it at least an hour and up to 2 days ahead.

350 g (12 oz) frozen
   dark sweet cherries

1 tsp cornflour

2 purple plums

100 g pack dried mixed berries
   and cherries, or a similar
   mix of unsweetened
   dried fruit

2 tsp ground cinnamon

1 tsp vanilla extract

squeeze of lemon juice

grated zest of 1 small orange

3 drops almond extract

6 sheets from a pack
   of filo pastry

olive oil

50 g (2 oz) ground almonds
   or hazelnuts

50 g (2 oz) brown breadcrumbs

Defrost frozen filo pastry overnight in the fridge. Drain the defrosted cherries in a colander set over a bowl to catch the juice. Mix the cornflour and a tablespoon of the cherry juice into a smooth cream (save the rest of the juice for smoothies).

Cut the pitted plums into cherry-sized pieces. Heat the well-drained fruit with the rest of the filling ingredients except the cornflour mixture in a small saucepan until steaming. Whisk in the cornflour and bring to a bubble, whisking until the mixture thickens then leave to cool.

To fill and bake, spread the nuts and breadcrumbs on a baking tray and place in a cold oven. Set the oven to 200°C/Gas 6 and toast the mixture while the oven heats up until golden, 5-10 minutes. Cut a sheet of baking paper 45 cm (18") wide and lay it on your work surface. Count out 6 sheets of filo pastry, then return the rest to the packet and chill or refreeze according to packet directions. Cover the 6 sheets of filo with a cloth to prevent them drying out.

Lay a sheet of the filo on the baking paper and quickly re-cover the rest with the cloth. Starting at the edges – which are the most prone to drying out – spritz or lightly brush the pastry all over with oil, then sprinkle lightly with some of the crumb mixture. Lay a second sheet of pastry on top, smoothing it out with your hands, then brush and crumb as before. Repeat this process until you have 6 layers.

Starting 7.5 cm (3") from the edge nearest to you, spread the filling in a 5 cm (2") wide band over the pastry, leaving 2.5 cm (1") clear at each end. Turn in the ends, then with the help of the paper, roll up the strudel like a Swiss roll. Make sure the ends are well tucked in and the strudel is seam-side down so the filling doesn't leak out, then carefully transfer the strudel and paper to the baking tray.

Spritz or lightly brush the top and sides of the filo with a final coating of oil. With a very sharp knife, make 6-8 diagonal cuts just through the top 3 layers of pastry to make the strudel easier to slice once baked. Bake at 200°C/Gas 6 for 25-30 minutes until crisp and golden brown. Serve warm.

JUDI'S TIP: the unbaked strudel can be frozen for up to a month, and baked shortly before serving. Freeze the filled, uncooked strudel on the baking sheet for 15 minutes, then cover with clingfilm and foil and freeze until needed. Bake from frozen in the oven at 190°C/Gas 5 for 35-45 minutes or until crisp golden brown and piping hot inside.

CHERRIES, PURPLE PLUMS AND RAISINS are rich in antioxidants that help fight cancer, heart disease, and dementia. They also reduce inflammation and joint pain.

JEWELLED CHOCOLATE & POMEGRANATE DISCS

Makes: 10-12
Eat within 1 day.
Keeps: 3 days at room temperature
if dried fruit, such as goji berries
or cherries, is used instead of the
pomegranate seeds.
Per serving: 93 cals, 6 g carbs

These indulgent, easy to make chocolate discs, with their irresistible mix of smooth dark chocolate, crunchy nuts and tangy fresh pomegranate seeds, are a healthy alternative to a box of chocolates and a rather beautiful after-dinner treat.

Unsweetened chocolate contains polyphenols, antioxidants that can help prevent heart disease, cancer, and Alzheimer's. Pomegranate seeds, which replace the sugar-laden glacé cherries traditionally used in Florentines, are rich in antioxidants and help control blood pressure. The nuts are a good source of protein, healthy fats and vitamins B and E.

Mixing melted and unmelted chocolate together (a process known as tempering) changes the structure of the chocolate, giving the finished discs a lovely glossy finish.

For a nut-free version, use cacao nibs, dried coconut pieces, or dried fruit such as sultanas, raisins, cherries, or chopped apricots instead of the pecans and pistachios.

---

100 g (3 ½ oz) good quality
  dark eating chocolate
  (70% cocoa if possible)
100 g (3 ½ oz) pecan halves
  or chopped pistachios,
  or a mixture
2 tbsp fresh pomegranate seeds

Line a tray with baking paper. Chop the chocolate into small pieces. Put two-thirds in a bowl and microwave on half power in 10-20 second bursts until just melted. Alternatively, melt it in a heat-proof bowl set over a saucepan of barely simmering water for 3-4 minutes, stirring occasionally, until almost melted then remove from the heat.

With either method, add the remaining third of unmelted chocolate to the bowl, mixing vigorously for a minute or two until smooth. If the mixture is still lumpy, warm it slightly, either by a 10-second burst in the microwave or over the hot water in the saucepan.

Working quickly before the chocolate starts to set, drop teaspoonfuls of the melted chocolate onto the paper, spreading each into a 5 cm (2") circle with the back of your spoon. Stud each disc with pomegranate seeds and the nuts or other toppings. Leave to set, but don't refrigerate or the chocolate will lose its shine.

JUDI'S TIP: as a short-cut, use a 100g pack of giant dark chocolate buttons instead of eating chocolate. Soften them slightly in the microwave, then arrange them on a lined baking sheet and add the toppings as before. The chocolate won't stay glossy but will taste fine.

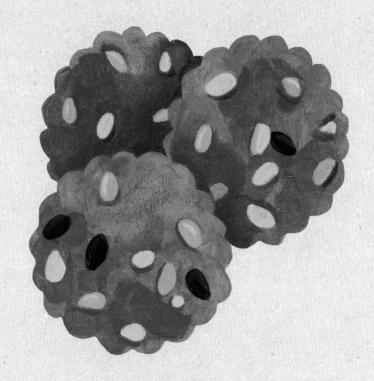

9 | BAKES

WHOLE GRAIN CHALLAH METUKAH

Makes 2 small or 1 large loaf
Keeps: 3-4 days
at room temperature
Freeze: 3 months baked,
or 2 weeks plaited
and ready to bake
Per serving: 245 cals, 33 g carbs

Every Friday morning, piles of delicious raisin-studded challah metukah, or sweet challah, appear in bakeries across Israel. Sadly, commercial challah is often loaded with additives and sugar, reason enough to make it at home, but challah is also fun to make. You can make it from start to finish in a couple of hours, but the flavour is best if the dough is allowed to rise slowly overnight. If serving with chopped egg and onion, use caraway seeds instead of raisins. Omit the sesame seeds if someone is allergic to sesame.

420 g (15 oz) whole grain
  seeded bread flour
140 g (5 oz) very strong
  white bread flour
  (Canadian is best)
  plus extra for kneading
2 sachets instant yeast
1 tsp fine sea salt
2 tbsp clear honey
240 ml (8 fl oz) warm water
80 ml (2 ¾ fl oz) olive oil
2 large eggs at room temperature
115 g (4 oz) sultanas or raisins,
  or 1 tbsp caraway seeds

For the glaze
1 tsp water
pinch of salt
2 tbsp poppy, sesame, caraway
  or flax seeds, or a mixture

Mix the dry ingredients in a stand mixer fitted with a dough hook on low speed (if using a food processor, you will need to make the dough in 2 or 3 batches). Mix in the honey, water and oil. Beat the eggs, reserving 2 tablespoons for the glaze, and add the rest to the dough. Mix or process until a ball begins to form, then increase the speed and mix for 3-4 minutes until the dough leaves the side of the bowl clean as it rotates. If not, reduce the speed and add more flour, a tablespoon at a time, until it does.

Tip the dough out onto a floured surface, add the dried fruit or seeds, and knead vigorously for 3 minutes until springy. Work in more flour if the dough feels sticky when squeezed. Transfer to a large bowl, cover with clingfilm or a plastic bag, and leave to rise until doubled in bulk, 45-60 minutes at room temperature, or up to 24 hours in the fridge.

Punch down the risen dough to break up any large bubbles, then divide into 3 equal portions for one large challah or into 6 for two smaller ones. Flatten each portion with your fist, then roll into a small Swiss roll. Flatten again, roll as before, then form into a ball – this greatly improves the texture of the finished loaf.

Roll each ball into a 30 cm (12") strand that tapers slightly at each end. For each challah, join 3 strands firmly together at one end, fan them out then plait into a loaf, pinching the ends together. Roll it gently on your work surface to even out the shape, then transfer to a baking paper-lined baking sheet. Whisk the reserved yolk, water and salt together, brush evenly over the challah and sprinkle generously with seeds. Slip the tray into a large plastic bag and leave to rise for 45 minutes to 1 hour, or until puffy.

Meanwhile, preheat the oven to 230°C/Gas 8. Bake the challah for 25-30 minutes until crusty and brown and the bottom sounds hollow when tapped, then transfer to a cooling rack.

> Pictured on previous page

JACKIE'S CARROT & CARDAMOM CAKE

Serves 8-10
Keeps: 1 week in the fridge
Freeze: 3 months
Per serving: 441 cals, 41 g carbs

With its gold and orange-hued sponge, this moist, tender cake is made with olive oil rather than the usual butter or margarine, and wholemeal flour for added fibre. Raisins and cranberries add natural sweetness, while a crunchy walnut and coconut topping replaces the traditional sugary cream cheese icing. Jackie has also replaced some of the sugar in her original recipe with erythritol (see page 8).

---

340 g (12 oz) carrots
175 ml (6 oz) olive oil
4 large eggs
75 g (2½ oz) dark soft brown sugar
8 tbsp erythritol
280 g (10 oz) wholemeal flour
2 tsp baking powder
1 tsp bicarbonate of soda
1 tsp vanilla extract
2 tsp cinnamon
pinch nutmeg
½ tsp ground cardamom
finely grated zest of 1 orange
  and 1 lemon
120 g (4 oz) raisins or sultanas
30 g (1 oz) unsweetened dried
  cranberries or cherries
140 g (5 oz) coarsely chopped
  walnuts

For the topping
1 tbsp unsweetened desiccated
  coconut

Preheat the oven to 180°C/Gas 4. Oil and line the bottom of a 23 cm (9") spring form or loose-bottomed cake tin with baking paper.

Peel and slice the carrots, then chop them finely in a food processor, scraping down the sides as needed. Add the oil then pulse to combine. Add all the remaining ingredients except the dried fruit, nuts and coconut. Process until evenly mixed, then pulse in the dried fruit and three-quarters of the nuts in 3-4 one-second bursts.

Turn the batter into the prepared tin then sprinkle with the remaining nuts and the desiccated coconut. Bake for 30-45 minutes or until a skewer inserted in the middle comes out clean. Serve plain, with a fruit compote, or Greek yoghurt.

CARROTS are good for healthy skin and eyes. Like other orange vegetables, they are rich in vitamin A, which can reduce the risk of night blindness, cataracts, and macular degeneration. They can also help lower blood pressure, protect the heart, and boost immunity. Eating carrots with olive oil or butter helps your body to absorb the vitamin A.

FEATHERLIGHT
LEMON KICHLACH

GRAB & GO
GRANOLA
BARS

PINE NUT
& CARDAMOM
BISCUITS

FRESH
GINGER FORK
BISCUITS

FEATHERLIGHT LEMON KICHLACH

NOT VEGAN

Makes: about 20
Keeps: 1 week in an airtight tin
Freeze: 3 months
Per serving: 69 cals, 8 g carbs

With the zing of fresh lemon and a delicate texture somewhere between a biscuit and a cake, these take moments to make. Measure the ingredients carefully and don't overbake.

1 large egg
75 ml (5 tbsp) olive oil
½ tsp vanilla or lemon extract
finely grated zest of 2 lemons
60 g (2 oz) caster sugar
85 g (3 oz) white self-raising flour
30 g (1 oz) wholemeal self-raising flour, or regular wholemeal plus ¼ tsp baking powder
pinch salt
chopped or slivered almonds or pistachios

Preheat the oven to 200°C/Gas 6. Lightly oil and line one large or two medium baking sheets with baking paper. In a large bowl, whisk the egg with the oil, vanilla and lemon zest. Add the sugar and whisk until thick, then add the flour and salt and mix thoroughly with a wooden spoon.

Drop tablespoons of the mixture no less than 5 cm (2") apart onto the prepared baking sheet – easiest with a smallish ice cream scoop – then sprinkle with the nuts. Bake for 8-10 minutes until pale gold and just tinged with brown at the edges.

GRAB & GO GRANOLA BARS

Makes: about 12 bars
Keeps: 1 week
at room temperature
in an airtight tin
Freeze: 3 months
Per serving: 220 cals, 25 g carbs

A brilliant on-the-go breakfast or lunch box pick-me-up, these flapjack style bars are packed with fibre that helps to balance the natural sugars in the honey. We like to use a mixture of chopped apricots, sultanas, goji berries, hazelnuts, sunflower and pumpkin seeds.

225 g (8 oz) rolled oats
3 tbsp each plain and wholemeal flour
1 tsp ground cinnamon
pinch ground nutmeg
60 g (2 oz) dried fruit
30 g (1 oz) roughly chopped nuts
1 tbsp mixed seeds
120 g (4 oz/½ cup) thin honey
1 large egg
120 ml (4 fl oz) melted coconut oil

Preheat the oven to 180°C/Gas 4. Lightly oil a 20 cm x 20 cm (8" × 8") baking tin and line with baking paper, cutting a small square out of each corner so the paper fits neatly into the tin.

Mix the dry ingredients with a pinch of salt in a large mixing bowl. Measure the oil in a jug then add your honey to make up to 240 ml (8 fl oz/1 cup). Add the egg to the jug, whisk with a fork, then pour onto the dry ingredients and mix well.

Transfer the mixture to the tin and spread out into an even layer with the back of a spoon or your hand. Bake for 20-25 minutes or until golden, then transfer the tin to a cooling rack. Leave for 5 minutes, then turn out onto a board and cut into bars.

> Pictured on previous page

FRESH GINGER FORK BISCUITS

NOT VEGAN

Makes: about 20
Keeps: 1 week
in an airtight tin
Freeze: 3 months
Per serving: 75 cals, 6.5 g carbs

Fresh and dried ginger gives these melt-in-the-mouth texture biscuits a wonderful depth of flavour. It also has powerful anti-inflammatory properties and can soothe the digestion.

115 g (4 oz) chilled butter
30 g (1 oz) wholemeal spelt flour
90 g (3 oz) self-raising flour
40 g (1½ oz) muscovado
   or dark soft brown sugar
3 tsp grated fresh ginger
1 tsp ground ginger

Preheat the oven to 180°C/Gas 4 and cut the butter into small pieces. Put the flour, sugar, and both gingers into a food processor and process until evenly mixed. Add the butter and process until a moist dough forms that can be gathered into a ball, about 60 seconds. Transfer to a work surface, pinch off pieces the size of a small walnut and roll between your palms into balls. Arrange 5 cm (2") apart on an ungreased baking sheet. Use a fork to press down firmly on each ball to form deep grooves. Each biscuit should be about 1 cm (⅜") thick. Bake for 15 minutes until golden brown.

PINE NUT & CARDAMOM BISCUITS

Makes: about 2 dozen
Keeps: 2 weeks
at room temperature
in an airtight tin, store when cold
Freeze: 3 months
Per serving: 77 cals, 7 g carbs

A nutty twist on Judebröd, traditional Danish-Jewish freeform cookies. For a dressier version, roll the dough into a thin disc, chill for 20 minutes, then use a biscuit cutter to cut out fancy shapes before baking. Ground cardamom quickly loses its flavour, so buy pods, release the seeds, then grind them as needed and store any extra in an airtight jar in the fridge. If allergic to nuts, use sunflower seeds instead.

30 g (1 oz) wholemeal flour
120 g (4 oz) self-raising flour
50 g (2 oz) light muscovado
   or soft brown sugar
1 tsp ground cardamom seeds
1 tsp ground cinnamon
120 g (4 oz) cold butter
60 g (2 oz) pine nuts

Preheat the oven to 180°C/Gas 4. Line 2 baking sheets with baking paper. Put the flour, sugar and spices in the food processor. Cut the butter into 1 cm (½") cubes, add to the flour mixture and process until the mixture begins to cling together in little balls, 30-45 seconds. Pulse in 2 tablespoons of the nuts. The dough should be like plasticine.

Pinch off pieces and roll between your palms into balls the size of a large marble. Arrange the balls at least 5 cm (2") apart on the baking sheets, flatten slightly with your fingers, then sprinkle with the remaining pine nuts and press into 6 mm (¼") thick discs with your fingers or the bottom of a glass. Bake for 15 minutes until set. Leave to cool for 10 minutes then carefully transfer to a cooling rack.

CITRUS & POLENTA CAKE

Serves: 8-10.
Keeps: 1 week in the fridge
Freeze: 3 months without the
orange topping
Per serving: 270 cals, 22 g carbs

A lovely torte inspired by an Evelyn Rose Passover recipe called Orange Blossom Cake. This version uses polenta or fine cornmeal, instead of matzah meal, so it's gluten-free. The delicate sponge is infused with fresh citrus and topped with fresh oranges.

3 large eggs
pinch of salt
1 lemon
2 oranges
1 tsp vanilla extract
50 g (2 oz) caster sugar
125 g (4 oz) ground almonds
50 g (2 oz) polenta
   or fine yellow cornmeal
1 tsp finely chopped fresh
   rosemary or lemon verbena
125 ml (4 fl oz) olive oil

To serve
2 oranges,
   ideally a mix of navel
   and blood orange

Preheat the oven to 180°C/Gas 4. Grease and line the base and sides of a 22 cm (9") diameter springform or loose-bottomed tin with baking paper.

Separate the eggs, putting the whites in a medium bowl and the yolks in a large one. Whisk the whites with a pinch of salt using an electric beater until they hold stiff but glossy peaks, then whisk in 1 teaspoon of the sugar.

Whisk the yolks with the remaining sugar for 2-3 minutes until pale and smooth – the mixture should fall from the whisk in a ribbon. Zest and juice the lemon and oranges, then add a tablespoon of the lemon juice, all the zest, and 4 tablespoons of the orange juice to the yolk mixture (reserve the rest of the juice). Using a rubber spatula fold in the ground almonds, polenta, rosemary or verbena, and oil.

Stir a quarter of the beaten egg white into the polenta mixture to lighten its texture, then delicately fold in the remaining whites with a rubber spatula. Gently coax into the prepared cake tin and smooth the top level.

Bake for 25-30 minutes or until golden and springy to gentle touch. Prick the top of the cake all over with a toothpick or fork, then pour over the reserved orange and lemon juice. Leave for 10-15 minutes, then run a knife round the edge and release the cake from the tin.

Up to 2 hours before serving, peel and thinly slice the oranges and arrange them decoratively on top of the cake. Serve at room temperature with Greek yoghurt, sorbet or low-sugar ice cream.

JUDI'S TIP: polenta is made from finely ground dried maize. It's sold in various forms — pre-cooked, quick-cook or natural which looks like coarse sand. For this recipe you need either natural polenta or fine yellow cornmeal, which is the same thing.

SUMMER BERRY BUCKLE

Serves: 8-10
Keeps: 2 days in the fridge
Freeze: 1 month
Per serving: 326 cals, 36 g carbs

A rich dense cake with a sweet buttery streusel topping, which contains so much fruit it almost "buckles" under the weight. Using strong flour in the batter gives the sponge just enough structure to support the fruit while remaining tender.

It's an old American recipe and blueberries are traditional, but other seasonal fruit like blackberries, raspberries, and peaches are all delicious. Don't use frozen fruit, which releases too much liquid during cooking and lacks the flavour and natural sweetness of fresh fruit. It's fine to omit the nuts in the topping though.

For the streusel topping

50 g (2 oz) very soft butter

70 g (2 ½ oz) wholemeal flour

1 tsp cinnamon

20 g (¾ oz) soft brown sugar

2 tbsp chopped walnuts, pecans or hazelnuts

For the cake batter

140 g (5 oz) soft butter

40 g (1 ½ oz) caster sugar or erythritol

1 tsp lemon zest

2 tsp vanilla extract

2 large eggs

200 g (7 oz) strong white bread flour

1 ½ tsp baking powder

500 g (1 ¼ lb) mixed berries (blueberries, raspberries and blackberries)

squeeze of fresh lemon juice

Preheat the oven to 180°C/Gas 4. Lightly grease a 20 cm (8") square or a 23 cm (9") round cake tin and line the bottom and two sides with a strip of baking paper.

Make the streusel topping by rubbing the butter into the flour, brown sugar and cinnamon by hand or food processor until it resembles coarse breadcrumbs. Add nuts, then squeeze the mixture with your hand to form small clumps.

To make the cake batter, cream the butter, sugar, salt, vanilla and lemon zest in a food processor or mixer for 2-3 minutes until light and fluffy, scraping down the sides with a spatula as needed.

Add the eggs then mix or process for another minute. The batter may look "split" but don't panic. Mix the flour and baking powder together then add to the batter and mix or pulse until there are no visible pockets of flour.

Toss the berries with a squeeze of lemon juice, then remove the blade or beater and gently fold the berries into the batter with a spatula. Turn the mixture into the tin – it will be thick – then coax into an even layer with your spatula and scatter with the streusel. Bake for 45-55 minutes until golden brown and a skewer inserted into the centre of the cake comes out clean.

Leave to cool for 5 minutes or so. Carefully lift out of the tin using the baking paper like a sling and transfer to a serving plate or board, then slide the paper out from underneath. If not serving immediately, store in the tin, well-wrapped with foil or clingfilm.

SUNRISE MUFFINS

Serves: 8
Keeps: 2 days
at room temperature
Freeze: 3 months
Per serving: 134 cals, 16 g carbs

Jackie first came across these fruity bran muffins in Canada during her medical student days, and later developed her own low sugar version using a combination of dark muscovado and erythritol (see page 8). They're lovely served freshly baked or briefly reheated in the microwave, and make a healthy addition to a lunch box.

Whole grains, sultanas, and seeds provide tons of fibre, which helps regulate blood sugar and lower cholesterol. Fibre is also excellent for maintaining digestive health and good gut bacteria.

4 rounded tbsp bran breakfast
cereal ("threads" not flakes)
finely grated zest and juice
of a small orange
1 medium carrot
50 g (1 ½ oz) melted
or very soft butter
50 g (2 oz) wholemeal flour
30 g (1 oz) rolled oats
30 g (1 oz) dark muscovado sugar
1 rounded tbsp erythritol
1 tsp baking powder
pinch of salt
½ tsp ground cinnamon
15 g (½ oz) sunflower seeds
45 g (1 ½ oz) sultanas or raisins
½ tsp bicarbonate of soda
100 ml (3 fl oz) milk
or unsweetened soya milk
1 large egg

Preheat the oven to 200°C/Gas 6 and line a 12 cup muffin tin with paper or reusable silicone cases. Put the orange zest, juice and bran in a bowl, stir well and leave to soak.

Trim, peel and roughly chop the carrot then add to the food processor and process until very finely chopped. Add the butter or oil and all the dry ingredients except the seeds, dried fruit and bicarbonate of soda. Process until evenly mixed.

Whisk the bicarbonate of soda with the milk and egg, then add to the batter and pulse briefly to mix. Add the soaked bran mixture and pulse again. Finally, stir or pulse in the seeds and dried fruit.

Divide the mixture evenly between the muffin cases (most easily done with an ice cream scoop). Bake for 15-18 minutes until light brown and springy on top, then transfer to a cooling rack.

JUDI'S TIP: for the best texture, let the milk and eggs come to room temperature for at least 15 minutes before mixing with the bicarbonate of soda.

FARMHOUSE SULTANA SCONES

Makes: 8-10 scones
Keeps: 2 days in the fridge
Freeze: raw for up to 1 month
Per serving: 126 cals, 21 g carbs

When Scottish settlers first emigrated to the States back in the nineteenth century, they had the idea of using newly-discovered baking powder to leaven their scones instead of the soda and sour milk used in their native land, and baked in an oven instead of the traditional hearth-top griddle. Enter the scone we now know and love, which is so easy to make at home.

This wholemeal version, studded with dried fruit, is made with yoghurt which gives a tender fluffy texture. Sultanas are also rich in boron, which may help reduce the risk of osteoporosis. A light sprinkling of cane sugar adds a delicious crunch to the top of the scones, but can be omitted. We love them freshly baked, split in half and topped with a schmear of butter and some fresh strawberries in place of the usual jam and clotted cream.

---

150 g (5 oz) wholemeal flour
75 g (3 oz) plain flour
3 tsp baking powder
2 tbsp dark muscovado sugar
3-4 tbsp sultanas or raisins
½ tsp salt
40 g (1½ oz) cool butter
130 g (4 ½ oz) plain yoghurt

For the topping
1 tsp plain yoghurt
1 tsp cane or demerara sugar

Preheat the oven to 220°C/Gas 7 and line a baking tray with baking paper. Cut the butter into small pieces.

To make the dough with a food processor, process the dry ingredients except the sultanas to mix, then add butter and process for 20 seconds or until the mixture looks like fine breadcrumbs. Transfer to a mixing bowl. To make by hand, mix all the dry ingredients except the sultanas in a bowl, then rub in the fat until the mixture resembles fine bread crumbs.

With either method, make a well in the centre of the flour mixture, add the yoghurt and sultanas, and mix gently to a soft dough with a round-ended knife, cutting through the dry ingredients to moisten them equally. Turn the dough out onto a lightly floured board and knead with your fingers for 20-30 seconds until no cracks remain.

Pat or roll the dough into a 2 cm (¾") thick disc, then cut into rounds with a 6 cm (2 ½") biscuit cutter or glass. Arrange on the baking tray, brush the tops with yoghurt and sprinkle with the sugar. Bake for 10-15 minutes, or until golden brown, then transfer the scones to a cooling rack.

JUDI'S TIP: nothing can compare with a freshly baked scone. You can store the dry mix, including the butter, in the fridge for several weeks then only the yoghurt needs adding to turn it into scone dough ready to shape and bake. Or freeze a batch of unbaked scones, defrost at room temperature, then pop them in the oven to bake when your guests arrive.

MARY'S FRUIT & NUT CAKE

Serves: 6-8
Keeps: 1-2 weeks
at room temperature
in an airtight tin
Freeze: 3 months
Per serving: 270 cals, 29 g carbs

115 g (4 oz) butter
   or 85 g (3 oz) coconut oil
50 g (2 oz) brown sugar
170 g (6 oz) currants
170 g (6 oz) sultanas
finely grated zest of 2 lemons
finely grated zest of 1 orange
1 heaped tsp ground allspice
1 tsp cinnamon
2 level tsp sodium bicarbonate
2 large eggs
pinch salt
1 tsp vanilla extract
½ tsp almond extract
115 g (4 oz) spelt flour
115 g (4 oz) self-raising flour
75 g (3 oz) pecans
   or walnuts

The Mary in question runs a dress shop in Lancashire, and helped Jackie choose the outfits for her children's Bar and Bat Mitzvahs. By coincidence, Mary's cake is very similar to Evelyn Rose's Farmhouse Fruit Cake. It's rich in fibre and protein, and perfect with a cup of tea.

At least an hour and up to a day before you plan to bake the cake, put the fat in a medium saucepan with the sugar, dried fruit, zest and spices. Dissolve the bicarbonate of soda in 230 ml (8 fl oz) hot water and add to the fruit, stirring well.

Bring the mixture to the boil, simmer for a minute then turn off the heat. Leave for 1-2 hours or overnight in a cool place for the fruit to plump up.

When you're ready to bake the cake, preheat the oven to 180°C/Gas 4 and line the bottom and sides of a 20 cm (8") loose-bottomed or springform cake tin with baking paper.

Chop the nuts coarsely and set aside a tablespoon for the topping. Add the remaining nuts and the rest of the ingredients to the fruit and stir well. Pour the mixture into the prepared cake tin and sprinkle with the reserved nuts.

Bake in the centre of the oven for 40-60 minutes until golden brown, and a skewer comes out clean from the centre. Take care not to overbake or the cake will be dry. Leave to cool in the tin for 5-10 minutes then turn out on to a cooling rack. When cool, wrap in foil and store in an airtight container.

DR JACKIE'S GUIDE
TO HEALTH & HAPPINESS

INTRODUCTION

As a family doctor, I've witnessed first hand the rise in chronic conditions such as obesity, cardiovascular disease, and type 2 diabetes, which research now clearly shows to be related to diet and lifestyle, not merely genetics. It's something about which I've grown increasingly concerned and motivated to help address.

This guide will give you detailed information about how what you eat can help you stay healthy, reduce your risk of the above conditions, and guard against cancer and dementia. You'll also find guidance on how to achieve and maintain a healthy weight and good mental health and why I consider sugar to be behind many illnesses of modern life.

There are special chapters on diet for those with conditions such as high blood pressure, high cholesterol, cancer, coeliac disease and Crohn's or other autoimmune illnesses. A special diet is not intended to replace medical treatment or advice from your doctor, but can help in the prevention of illness, or alongside prescribed medications.

I've spent years reading articles, research papers and books on nutrition. That said, this is not a precise science. Even the most rigorous research often relies on questionnaires in which participants are asked to recall the details of their diet from days or weeks previously. What they eat needs to be tracked over many years to see the impact on their health, and even then, it can be hard to prove cause and effect.

New discoveries are being made all the time, so this cannot be a definitive guide. I have tried to make the best sense of the research as it currently stands and, I hope, help you and your family to lead long and healthy lives.

JACKIE ROSE, MbChB, MRCGP, DCH, DRCOG

MEDICAL GLOSSARY

Alzheimer's Disease A common form of dementia that may come on gradually in middle age or old age, typically beginning with short-term memory loss.

Antioxidants Chemicals within foods and occurring naturally in the body that help fight disease and stabilise damaging molecules known as free radicals.

Autoimmune Disease An illness in which the body's natural defences or immune system damage the body's own tissues.

Carbohydrate A macronutrient found in grains, vegetables, legumes, and fruits. The main types of carbohydrates are sugars, starches, and fibre.

Carcinogen Any material or chemical that increases the risk of developing cancer.

Cruciferous Vegetables A class of vegetables with X-shaped flowers that can reduce inflammation and may lower the risk of cancer.

Coeliac Disease An autoimmune condition where you react to gluten in the diet with various symptoms often including weight loss, bloating, and anaemia.

Complex Carbohydrates These carbohydrates are unrefined, high in fibre, and raise the blood sugar more slowly than simple sugars.

Crohn's Disease An autoimmune chronic illness where there is inflammation of the lining of the bowel wall.

DHA and EPA Long-chain molecules of Omega-3, mostly derived from fish or algae, used by the brain within nerve cell membranes.

Diabetes Type One This type of diabetes most often begins in childhood or as a young adult. The pancreas produces little or no insulin, so insulin injections are needed.

Diabetes Type Two Here both blood sugar and insulin levels become progressively raised, and the tissues no longer respond to insulin as they should. It is often caused by obesity.

Fatty Acids The building blocks of fats, produced when fats are broken down by digestion.

Free Radicals Unstable molecules within the cells that can set off chain reactions, damaging tissues. They are balanced out by antioxidants.

Fibre Complex carbohydrates that are poorly digested. They have various health benefits such as reducing the risk of heart disease, diabetes, and cancer. Fibre may act as a prebiotic, fuel for good gut bacteria.

Gluten A protein found in wheat and other grains including rye, spelt, and barley. Intolerance of gluten is a feature of coeliac disease.

Glucose A simple refined carbohydrate formed, together with fructose, when table sugar is digested. It is used as a fuel within the body, especially the brain.

HDL Cholesterol A molecule formed from cholesterol and protein that helps transport cholesterol away from the heart to the liver, which may reduce damage to the arteries.

Hippocampus A structure found on both sides of the brain with an important role in short and long-term memory and learning.

Hypertension Persistently raised blood pressure.

Inflammation The reaction of the body to an injury or infection, or due to an autoimmune disease. It can cause soreness, pain, tenderness, or swelling. Lasting inflammation may cause chronic disease.

Inflammatory Bowel Disease A group of autoimmune illnesses, including Crohn's Disease, where the bowel wall is inflamed.

Ischaemic Heart Disease A condition in which the coronary arteries supplying the walls of the heart become narrowed. It can cause episodes of chest pain called angina and lead to heart attacks.

LDL Cholesterol A molecule containing cholesterol and protein that delivers cholesterol to the tissues, including the heart, and may be a risk for narrowing of the arteries.

Lipids A term for fats, which includes cholesterol and triglycerides.

Melatonin A naturally occurring hormone needed for a healthy sleep-wake cycle.

Microbiome The range of bacteria, fungi, and other microorganisms that live in and on our bodies, especially the gut and skin.

Monounsaturated Fats A type of fatty acid where the carbon chain has a single double bond. These fats help reduce the risk of ischaemic heart disease and dementia.

Neurogenesis A process where new nerve cells (neurons) are formed from stem cells. In adults, this occurs in the hippocampus area of the brain.

Non-coeliac Gluten Intolerance A condition in which various symptoms improve when gluten is removed from the diet.

Omega-3 Polyunsaturated fatty acids, such as DHA and EPA. from fish and seafood, or alpha-linolenic acid (ALA), from nuts and seeds. Beneficial to the heart and brain, they may also reduce the risk of cancer.

Omega-6 Polyunsaturated fatty acids, including linoleic acid (LA), found in nuts, seeds, meat, eggs, and dairy products. Beneficial to the heart and brain, but excess omega-6 may compete with omega-3. Refined forms of omega-6 are less healthy.

Polyunsaturated Fats In this type of fatty acid there are multiple double bonds between the carbon atoms. Polyunsaturated fatty acids include omega-3 and omega-6.

Prebiotics High fibre foods that act as fuel for good gut bacteria.

Probiotics Fermented foods, including live natural yoghurt, kefir, sauerkraut, kimchi, and some supplements, which supply extra bacteria to boost the body's good gut bacteria.

Protein A macronutrient vital for the formation and growth of bones, muscles, and organs.

Refined Carbohydrates Carbohydrates that have been processed and therefore lower in nutrients and fibre than complex carbs, and more damaging to our health. See also White Carbs.

Saturated Fats Heat stable fatty acids found in meat and dairy products, coconut and palm oil, with no double bond between the carbon atoms.

Serotonin A chemical messenger that occurs naturally in the brain. Many medicines for depression aim to increase the level of serotonin.

Triglyceride A lipid formed by linking three fatty acids with a glycerol chain. Raised triglyceride levels may be linked with excess visceral fat, and are a risk for ischaemic heart disease and pancreatitis.

Tryptophan An amino acid found in meat, nuts, and other protein-rich foods, that can be converted to serotonin and melatonin.

White Carbs Refined carbohydrates found in sugar, white flour, white pasta, white rice, and potatoes. They cause a rapid rise in blood sugar and insulin, and can lead to health problems including heart disease and diabetes.

THE POWER OF PLANTS

WHY PURPLE IS THE NEW GREEN

I grew up being told to "eat your greens" because the health benefits of green fruit and vegetables were already well known. In recent years, scientists have discovered that purple and red vegetables and fruits are particularly high in potent antioxidants called anthocyanins. For this reason, I recommend that you cook with red onions rather than white, and red cabbage, purple-fleshed plums, aubergines, blueberries, purple sweet potatoes and any other purple produce. Greens are still an important part of a healthy diet, but purple foods may now have the upper hand.

PHYTOCHEMICALS

These are the active elements in fruits and vegetables that we need to maintain a balanced metabolism, and include vitamins and antioxidants. I like to think of phytochemicals (from the Greek word, phyton, for plant) as "fighter chemicals" because they battle disease. They are quite remarkable.

Traditional chicken soup – with its heady mix of carrot, leek, celery, and onions – packs a hefty phytochemical punch, perhaps that's why it's known as "Jewish penicillin." Because vegetables contain less natural sugar than fruits, most nutritionists recommend that the former dominate your Five-a-Day. This is why vegetable-based smoothies are even healthier than those with just fruit.

ANTIOXIDANTS

Food-based antioxidants are important for reducing the risk of heart disease, cancer and dementia. They occur naturally in fruit and vegetables as well as tea – especially green tea – and coffee. When our body burns food for energy, it produces free radicals, molecules with an unpaired electron that may damage cells, causing disease and ageing. Antioxidants help to "mop up" these excess free radicals. They occur naturally in our bodies but sometimes not in large enough amounts to balance out the free radicals. Enter their plant-based counterparts, which boost our natural antioxidant defences. Hence the importance of eating your five – or better still, seven – servings of fruit and veg a day.

PHYTOCHEMICALS

Aubergine protects the brain and spinal cord. It also helps against arthritis and possibly dementia.

Blueberries lower blood pressure and reduce the risk of diabetes, heart disease, and stroke.

Cabbage, broccoli, cauliflower, and **rocket** can give protection against stomach ulcers and may help reduce the risk of cancer.

Carrots are good for your eyes and skin.

Celery helps prevent fluid retention and ankle swelling.

Garlic helps prevent blood clots and reduce blood pressure. It may improve cholesterol balance and treat colds.

Leeks nurture good gut bacteria, prevent blood clots, and may help reduce the risk of cancer.

Onions help circulation and protect against blood clots, and may improve asthma symptoms.

Tomatoes may help reduce the risk of cancer and osteoporosis.

PHENOMENAL FIBRE

Fibre is often underrated, but is forgotten at our peril. It reduces the risk of obesity, diabetes, raised cholesterol, heart disease, stroke, and colon cancer. It's also important for good digestion. Fibre is the part of plants that is not easily digested in the small intestine so travels to the large intestine, where it acts as a prebiotic - a fuel for beneficial gut bacteria. It can also be produced by a chemical change when starchy foods (white carbs) such as potatoes, pasta, or bagels are cooked, then chilled or frozen. This type of fibre is called resistant starch, and produces a lower spike in your blood sugar than the food would otherwise have done before chilling.

Soluble fibre can dissolve in water, forming a gel. It is found in apples, pears, legumes, lentils, raisins, and nuts. Insoluble fibre does not dissolve and passes through to the large bowel unchanged. It is found in whole grains, root vegetables and many other vegetables and plants, including brown rice.

DRESS UP YOUR SALADS

Dressed salads are a wonderful "one-stop" source of fibre, phytochemicals, and antioxidants, when made with healthy fats, such as extra virgin olive oil, avocado oil, or organic rapeseed oil. When these oils are combined with cider vinegar or lemon juice, they make a healthy and delicious base for a salad dressing. By contrast, shop-bought, processed salad dressings are often sweetened with sugar and may contain inferior refined oils.

The more additions to your dressing - fresh herbs, garlic, mustard and black pepper, the greater the benefits to your health. Salads made with sugar-free homemade dressings not only taste great but should not cause weight gain. They keep you feeling full for longer and so reduce the risk of snacking afterwards. If your salad contains tomatoes, the oil in your delicious dressing will also help your body absorb the antioxidant lycopene that they contain.

YOUR HIGH FIBRE DAY

Aim to eat at least 30 grams of fibre a day. Here are some ideas:

BREAKFAST

Rainbow Smoothie Bowl page 54
Sunrise Muffin page 210
A thick slice of wholemeal toast with sugar-free peanut butter
Porridge with berries or sliced banana

LUNCH

Moroccan Lentil Soup page 28
Jerusalem Hummus page 58
Katsis Kishuim page 60 with whole grain toast
Jewelled Quinoa Salad page 91
Roasted Vegetable Kugel page 100 with a green salad

SNACK

A handful of Crunchy Spiced Chickpeas page 71 or unsalted unsweetened nuts
Grab and Go Granola Bar page 204
An unpeeled apple

DINNER

Za'atar Crusted Fish page 125
Cottage Pie with a Twist page 156
Alsace Lentils page 170
Seasonal Stir-fried Greens page 172
A fresh pear, peach or nectarine

THE TRUTH ABOUT SUGAR

Cutting down on sugar is perhaps the single biggest step towards a healthier diet.

In his ground-breaking book, Pure, White and Deadly, Professor John Yudkin illustrates the links between this every day and often hidden part of our diet to coronary artery disease, including angina, as well as obesity and type 2 diabetes. Linked with the latter two conditions may be increases in the risk for raised blood pressure, fatty liver, raised LDL (bad) cholesterol, stroke, cancer, and dementia.

The NHS advises that adults should have no more than seven teaspoons (28 grams/1 oz) of sugar a day. Most of us consume nearly three times this amount because so much is hidden in shop-bought food and drink. Children aged seven to ten should not exceed six teaspoons (24 grams/0.85 oz) of sugar a day and those aged four to six should not go over five daily teaspoons (20 grams/0.7 oz). Younger infants should have as little as possible. The commonest reason for children to have a general anaesthetic is to remove multiple teeth because of the long term effects of sugary foods, drinks, and sweets.

If you want to save your children from much expense and misery, avoid giving them a sweet tooth from the beginning. Starting kids off on a healthy diet and explaining the benefits of eating well from a young age may help set eating patterns and health outcomes for the rest of their lives. But don't be too strict, or they may rebel! Children tend to follow your example, so practice what you preach.

Sugary drinks, especially sodas, increase the chance of gum disease and losing your teeth in later life, not to mention risk of type 2 diabetes. Over seven thousand amputations are carried out each year in the UK, many as a result of type 2 diabetes brought on by eating too much sugar.

THE GLYCAEMIC INDEX

When you consume sugary foods or drinks, sugar and insulin levels in your blood spike rapidly. An hour or so later you'll experience a sharp fall in your blood sugar level that will make you feel hungry again. Foods that cause this effect are said to have a high glycaemic index (GI). Some people are particularly sensitive to carbohydrates, resulting in higher sugar spikes, which increase their risk of type 2 diabetes.

HIDDEN SUGAR

Around three-quarters of all processed foods contain added sugar, especially biscuits, cakes and fruit yoghurt. Savoury foods such as baked beans, ketchup, packaged snacks, sauces and soups, even smoked salmon, are often high in sugar.

Breakfast cereals, especially frosted and chocolate flavoured ones, tend to have a particularly high sugar content. It is these that are intensively marketed for children. Wholegrain unsweetened cereals such as shredded wheat, Weetabix, low-sugar granola or porridge are healthier breakfast alternatives, unless you are following a low carb diet. Beware though: some makes of instant porridge – especially the kind you heat in a microwave –contain sugary syrups.

Many foods labelled "low-fat" or "light" are often full of sugar. The label will give grams of sugar per 100 grams. If this is 25 grams out of 100 grams, not unusual for a breakfast cereal, then a quarter of the packet is sugar (although if it contains dried fruit, this will also include the naturally occurring sugar in the fruit). So read labels carefully and don't assume that something is OK just because the description uses words that suggest health and fitness.

Drinks are a major source of "hidden" sugars, especially fizzy drinks such as cola, lemonade, and ginger beer. Just one can of cola contains more than eight teaspoons of sugar. "Energy drinks" often contain even more, merely adding "empty" calories to your diet. Adding flavoured syrups to coffee has much the same effect.

Fresh, unsweetened fruit juice is surprisingly high in sugar, often containing four teaspoons per glassful. It's worth diluting a third of a glass of juice with water to reap the benefits of the vitamin C without so much sugar.

White sugar is over 99% sucrose that breaks down into glucose and fructose during digestion. Glucose causes the pancreas to produce insulin to control the sudden rise in blood sugar.

Fructose has a lower glycaemic index, but in the long term, may be more harmful for the metabolism. Fructose is the main sugar found in fruits. When the whole fruit is eaten, the natural fibre protects against the negative effects of fructose. Fructose sold as 'fruit sugar' is not a healthier choice than table sugar.

ARTIFICIAL SWEETENERS

Many people substitute sweeteners for sugar. If you are diabetic, this may be a reasonable compromise, as sugar will be more harmful for you than sweeteners. However, most so-called diet or sugar-free drinks use aspartame, an artificial sweetener with a mixed record. Some studies suggest that if taken regularly, it may cause nerve damage or even cancer. Artificial sweeteners may also cause cravings for sweet foods or suppress your good gut bacteria.

It's better to cut back on both sugar and sweeteners by choosing still or unflavoured sparkling water, unsweetened tea and coffee, and plain milk, rather than flavoured variations. Herbs or slices of fresh fruits infused in cold or hot water are also an excellent choice.

HONEY & "NATURAL" SWEETENERS

Honey contains fructose, glucose, maltose and sucrose, but no fibre. It boasts antioxidants and a chemical called propolis, which is antibacterial. It is best when 'raw' as it keeps its natural enzymes, but should not be considered a health food. While not as harmful as high fructose corn syrup (present in many processed foods), honey should nonetheless be saved for an occasional treat.

Maple syrup and coconut sugar also provide some antioxidants, but in all other respects, act like sugar. Agave is a popular sugar alternative, but has a higher proportion of fructose than table sugar so is not a healthier choice. Stevia, produced from the leaves of the stevia plant, has little effect on your weight, blood sugar, and insulin levels and does not contribute to dental cavities. It may, however, have a bitter after-taste.

Erythritol and xylitol are forms of carbohydrates known as polyols. These are much lower in calories than sugar, raise blood sugar less, and are good for oral health. They may not suit some people who have irritable bowel syndrome, but erythritol is the better tolerated. They both occur naturally in some fruits and vegetables, and are commercially produced, usually from corn. We know that sugar is harmful. On the basis of current knowledge, erythritol, stevia, and xylitol seem to be the safest alternatives, but perhaps the best approach is to minimise them all.

SUGAR STRATEGIES

* If sweetness is needed, substitute
  erythritol, stevia, or xylitol, or use
  part sugar and part sweetener

* Substitute fruit, vegetable sticks,
  or nuts for snacks and nosh

* Make your own sauces, syrups
  and dressings to control the sugar

* Give children raisins, berries,
  baby tomatoes, or pieces of fruit
  instead of sweets

* Don't linger near the buffet table
  at parties and celebrations

* Scoop icing, buttercream,
  and jam off cakes

* Don't feel you have to serve
  multiple desserts to guests;
  a beautifully laid out fruit platter
  can be just as impressive

* Ask friends and relatives not
  to tempt you with sugary foods

* Share with a friend and have half
  a dessert each

* Forfeit sweetened sodas,
  flavoured milk, and sugary cereals

* Avoid bottled teriyaki sauce,
  which is mostly sugar - it's like
  pouring treacle over your meal

* Check the label: four grams
  of sugar equals one teaspoon

ALCOHOL

A folk tale about a wise man and his grandson. "I feel as if there are two wolves fighting within me, one gentle and helpful, the other angry, aggressive and unhappy," said the old man. "Which one will triumph?" asked his grandson. The wise man replied, "whichever one I feed."

Alcohol, derived from the fermentation of natural sugars in grain, fruit, or vegetables, is like sugar's evil twin. Beer is high in carbs, wine and spirits lower. As for sugar, so for alcohol. It leads to all the health risks of sugar such as diabetes, heart disease, liver disease, and cancer, but also has a negative effect on your brain and mood, amplifying anxiety, depression, causing "brain fog" and sleep disorders.

You might compare the long term effects on the brain of over-drinking to taking a finely tuned car engine designed to run on unleaded fuel and pouring in diesel. Drinking alcohol regularly, in significant amounts, can cause short and long-term harm, even if you don't think that you have a problem. Its effects are slow and subtle, but over time, can make the drinker angrier, unhappier, and less empathetic.

A major study from Oxford University, conducted over 30 years, showed that even moderate alcohol intake can cause shrinkage of the grey matter in the brain, especially in the hippocampus, which is central to memory formation. Alcohol also interferes with the beneficial action of omega-3 and may "wash it out" from the brain (see page 253).

Studies have shown that small amounts of alcohol can be beneficial to health. A very small glass of red wine a day may protect the heart, thanks to the grape-based antioxidant, resveratrol. But just as overeating sugar-containing foods can lead to type 2 diabetes and the need to give up sugar, long-term over-use of alcohol, can lead to dependency and to health problems such as heart failure and cirrhosis, life-threatening conditions that mean giving up alcohol altogether.

* Frequent drinking of alcohol can shrink the part of your brain that forms memories

* Too much alcohol is harmful, although small amounts of red wine may be good for your heart

* Treat alcohol with respect and it can be enjoyed in small amounts throughout your life

FATS: THE GOOD THE BAD AND THE UGLY

DAIRY FATS

Dairy products contain nutrients such as vitamins A, B, D, E, K1 and K2, protein, antioxidants and minerals, including calcium. They may offer some protection against osteoporosis and diabetes and help blood pressure. However, they should be taken in moderation due to the saturated fats (see page 248).

BUTTER VERSUS MARGARINE

Butter is a natural product, which is high in saturated fat and contains butyrate, which helps to reduce the risk of bowel cancer. Spread it thinly. Margarine, by contrast, is highly processed and may contain damaged oils and emulsifiers. These can cause general inflammation in the body and, if taken frequently, could help to provoke inflammatory bowel disease, although more research is needed on this.

DAIRY FATS & SUGAR

Combining saturated fat with sugar (or other refined carbs) is not recommended. So plain, unsweetened, cream in moderation may be fine, but cream cakes, pavlova, cheesecake, and ice cream are best kept for the occasional treat. Studies have shown that in the presence of a very low carbohydrate diet, dairy fat may have minimal impact on saturated fat levels in the blood.

ORGANIC MILK

Cattle used for organic milk are generally grass-fed and not given antibiotics. Their milk provides a better balance of fats and vitamins. Although more expensive, I recommend it, especially for pregnant and breastfeeding women.

DAIRY PRODUCTS & CHILDREN

Parents used to give their children skimmed or semi-skimmed milk to try to reduce their cholesterol. However, it has since been found that full cream milk can help to optimise growth and reduce obesity in children. This richer milk has more vitamins and is now preferred for young (pre-school) children. Milk has less fat than many people might think: whole milk has only 3.6% fat and semi-skimmed milk contains 1.7% fat.

MEAT & POULTRY FATS

Red meat appears to be less good for the heart than dairy fats. However, meat has other benefits, such as high protein and minerals, including iron. Most of us eat too much red meat. Meat from grass-fed or organically pastured cows is better than from grain-fed cows, because it provides more omega-3 and conjugated linoleic acid (CLA), an omega-6 fat which may help your metabolism.

Fortunately, most UK beef is grass-fed, especially through spring and summer, but imported meat may not be. Choose lean meat and remove excess fat and loose skin from chicken before cooking to reduce the number of calories. Avoid processed (deli) meat because it is generally higher in salt and preservatives and increases the risks for heart disease, type 2 diabetes and cancer.

HOME-MADE SALAD DRESSINGS

Delicate healthy oils, like cold-pressed extra virgin olive oil, omega-3-rich flaxseed oil, or walnut oil, are at their best when raw. They are excellent for salad dressings or to drizzle liberally over food. Extra virgin olive oil may be used for gentle frying, but has the most health benefits when unheated.

GENTLE FRYING

From a health perspective, you may wish to use cold-pressed rapeseed oil for frying. Unlike refined oils, this is not chemically altered or degraded by the manufacturing process. It contains monounsaturated fat, and a good balance of omega-3 to omega-6. It is a key part of the Nordic diet, which, like the Mediterranean diet has good health credentials.

In many parts of the Mediterranean, extra virgin olive oil is routinely used for frying. Although it has a lower smoke point than rapeseed oil, its disadvantages in cooking are offset by its high levels of antioxidants and the rich fruit and vegetable diet typical in this part of the world. Cold-pressed or extra virgin oils can be more expensive but the health benefits of avoiding refined oils may be very significant. To make a little of your healthy oil go a long way, buy a mister or spray bottle to fill with good quality oil.

In recent years, refined sunflower oil has become popular for cooking, and is now widely used in margarines and spreads. However, it has a lower smoke point and is higher in omega-6 than rapeseed oil, so when used for frying is more likely to oxidise, releasing harmful compounds.

STIR FRYING

The risks of altering fats through heating are greater at high temperatures, and even more so when the same oil is used repeatedly. Many fast food outlets and chip shops reuse the oil several times before it's thrown out, so you can draw your own conclusions about the wisdom of buying food there.

Try to avoid deep fat and high-temperature frying if you can. Eating less fried foods and reducing the amount of oil used will also help to reduce your calorie intake, with greater benefit for your heart. Other forms of cooking - steaming, grilling, or baking - are generally a healthier choice, although vegetable-based stir fries and quick sautés using reduced amounts of oil are thought to be fine.

For this type of cooking, it appears safest to use cold-pressed rapeseed oil or a saturated fat like virgin coconut oil. These fats are more stable at high-temperatures. Coconut oil contains lauric acid, which appears to benefit your metabolism and reduce visceral fat, however as coconut oil is high in saturated fat it should not be over-used.

ROASTING

If you roast potatoes or other vegetables, use a silicone pastry brush or spray to coat the vegetables very lightly with oil, and don't over-brown them.

SUPPLEMENTS: WHO NEEDS THEM?

Most people don't need supplements because they get enough nutrients through their diet. Supplements are not regulated as strictly as prescription drugs, and may be ineffective or interact with other supplements or medicines. That said, if you are not eating a nutritionally balanced diet, especially if you are vegan, or not getting enough sun on your skin, (for vit D), the following supplements might be suitable.

OMEGA-3

Omega-3 (as DHA and EPA) is important for heart and brain health, reducing your risk of developing an irregular heartbeat, having a heart attack, or developing dementia. The best sources of omega-3 by far are fish and algae. It is also found in nuts and seeds, although less than 1% of the omega-3 contained in these tends to reach the brain. If you are vegan or vegetarian, consider adding an algae oil supplement to your diet. Non-vegetarians could consider a fish-oil based supplement if they are not eating fish at least twice a week.

CLIMB YOUR K2

Vitamin K2 helps strengthen bones and appears to help reduce the amount of calcium laid down in artery walls, lowering the risk of a heart attack. A vitamin K2 supplement may also help reduce the risk of multiple sclerosis, cancer, dementia, and nerve pain. Vitamin K2 is found in fermented foods such as sauerkraut and kefir and to a lesser extent in egg yolks, dairy products, and liver. Most of us lack enough vitamin K2 in our diet. Unless you eat large amounts of fermented foods, a supplement may be helpful. Vitamin K2 may also be a good idea for those taking statins, which can reduce the levels of vitamin K2 in the body. A word of caution: research on vitamin K2 is in its infancy. It may interfere with some anticoagulants. Be sure to ask for "vitamin K2" because "K2" alone is a form of marijuana!

VITAMIN B12

B12 is important for brain and nerve function, including memory. It is found in animal products such as red meat, chicken, fish, eggs, and milk. Yeast extract flakes and spreads such as reduced-salt Marmite and chlorella, a form of algae, are also sources of B12. An annual blood test will show if you are getting enough B12 in your diet. I recommend a B12 supplement for vegans and vegetarians who are not regularly consuming yeast extract or chlorella, and to take advice on dosage. Older people should also have blood tests, (even non-vegetarians) as their absorption of B12 is often reduced.

VITAMIN D

Vitamin D helps regulate calcium and phosphate in the body, and is important for healthy teeth, bones, and muscles. Vitamin D deficiency is common. It often explains aches and pains and low mood, contributes to reduced immunity, and possibly also an increased risk for cancer. Most vitamin D comes from sunlight. Spend time in the sun, although make sure that you use sunblock to prevent skin cancer. This will usually allow enough ultraviolet B light to come through for vitamin D production.

Food sources of vitamin D include fatty fish, eggs (especially the yolks), liver, cheese, and, to a lesser extent, fortified milk and juice. It may be helpful to take a vitamin D supplement during the winter (or at any time, if you are housebound), but be careful not to exceed the recommended adult dose, which is usually ten micrograms (400 units) daily.

AHIFLOWER OIL

This seed oil contains stearidonic acid, a form of omega-3 that is converted into long-chain EPA and can help prevent depression.

CALCIUM

Calcium helps prevent osteoporosis and lowers blood pressure. It is readily available in many foods, such as dairy products, sardines, tahini, dark green vegetables, chia seeds, almonds, and organic soya. It is often combined with vitamin D in supplements, but I advise my patients to get calcium from their diet and take only the vitamin D as a supplement. When calcium is taken as a supplement, there is a risk of the dose being too high and of it being deposited in your arteries. Your doctor may monitor your calcium level through blood tests, especially if you are a vegan.

IODINE

This is important for your thyroid. Without adequate iodine, your metabolism can slow down, causing tiredness and weight gain. Milk and fish are the main dietary sources of iodine. Lima and pinto beans contain lower levels. Ask your doctor about iodine intake if you have a thyroid condition, raised blood pressure or kidney disease. Vegans might consider taking a daily supplement of up to 0.5 milligrams.

TURMERIC

A potent antioxidant and anti-inflammatory, this should be a regular part of your diet, ideally taken with black pepper and fat to boost absorption. Turmeric powder can be added to soups, sauces, curries, coffee, milk, or yoghurt. Alternatively, you can take a daily turmeric capsule.

CHOLINE

Choline is a vitamin-like essential nutrient important for the production of DNA, the maintenance of a healthy brain and nervous system. It may also help to prevent dementia in older people. Choline is found in fish, eggs and liver, and in smaller amounts in cauliflower, broccoli, and lecithin powder.

IRON & ZINC

Iron should ideally come from your diet (see page 278). Zinc is important for wound healing, growth, the work of enzymes, and preventing dementia. It is present in many foods but especially in meat, fish, nuts, seeds, legumes, mushrooms, and eggs. It is important not to exceed the recommended daily dose of zinc in a supplement as it can be toxic.

SUPPLEMENTS FOR VEGANS

Usually recommended	Sometimes recommended
* Omega-3	* Ahiflower Oil.
* Vitamin B12	* Calcium
* Iodine	* Zinc
* Choline	* Iron
* Vitamin D	
* Vitamin K2	

A HEALTHY WEIGHT

I believe that eating for health is more important than focussing on your weight and figure. Losing some weight and keeping it off is likely to be a side effect of a healthy diet, and often far more successful than "going on a diet" or strict calorie counting, which is really difficult to continue for a long time. If you are significantly overweight, losing weight gradually can make you healthier and reduce your risk of chronic illnesses, especially diabetes and cancer, as well as being helpful for mental health and self-esteem.

MORE FIBRE, LESS SUGAR

In his seminal book Fat Chance: The Hidden Truth About Sugar, Obesity and Disease, paediatric endocrinologist, Professor Robert Lustig, observes that the two best strategies for losing weight are to cut down sugar and sweetened drinks, and to eat more fibre. Dietary fibre, Lustig notes, releases a hormone from the stomach called PYY, which helps us stop overeating. On the other hand, lots of sugary food and drink can cause resistance to leptin, a hormone that signals to the brain when we are full.

Professor Lustig advises his patients, clinically obese children, to avoid sodas and fruit juice, and eat very few biscuits, sweets and cakes. His young patients drink mostly water and milk and eat wholegrain rather than white bread and lots of fruit and vegetables. With additional emotional support, they usually shed their extra pounds. There is strong evidence that sugary drinks cause weight gain. In fact the risk of obesity is increased by 1.6 times for every additional sugar-sweetened drink per day, even in physically active children.

THE MOST IMPORTANT MEAL OF THE DAY

A good breakfast of slow-burning foods such as porridge without sugar, an omelette, or plain full-fat yoghurt with berries and nuts, is a great way to set you up for the day, and reduce later "fressing" or over-eating.

THE MEDITERRANEAN DIET VERSUS A LOW CARB, HIGH FAT DIET

The Mediterranean diet is good for weight loss, but is particularly effective in combination with a very low sugar and relatively low carbohydrate intake. For a study carried out in Dimona, Israel between 2005 and 2007, Professor Iris Shai and colleagues of Ben Gurion University divided over 300 participants into three groups. One group followed a Mediterranean diet; the second a low carb, high (healthy) fat diet; and the third a high carb, low-fat, (low-calorie) diet.

The group on the Mediterranean diet found this diet easy to continue long term, lost weight, and registered the best reduction in pre-diabetes. The group on the low carb, high fat regimen, which featured healthy fats such as olive oil and omega-3 from fish but no red meat, also lost weight and ended up with the best cholesterol levels. The group on the low-fat, high carb diet had the worst long-term outcomes.

THERMOGENESIS & FAT BURNERS

Some foods including chillies, green tea, and bell peppers increase the burning of fat, boost metabolism and help weight loss. The effect is minor but can be helpful when combined with other weight-loss measures. Eating extra protein, especially if combined with omega-3, also helps sustain weight-loss and maintain muscle mass when dieting.

INTERMITTENT FASTING

Following a strict calorie-restricted diet for one or two days every week is gaining in popularity and many people manage to keep going with it in the long term. Besides weight loss, research suggests that it may also lower the risk of cancer, diabetes and dementia, and lead to lower cholesterol. Intermittent fasting does not suit everyone, particularly if you have a chronic health condition or are prone to dizziness or fainting, so it's important to discuss it with your GP.

TIME-RESTRICTED EATING

Many people are now choosing to eat within a time window and not snack outside these hours. Having an early evening meal then not eating again until breakfast, ideally about 12-14 hours later, is the best way to achieve this. The benefits are similar to those of intermittent fasting, but both forms of fasting may be unsuitable for some people. See also pages 255 and 260.

CUTTING OUT BREAD & OTHER CARBS

About 40-50% of us are sensitive to carbohydrates, including those with pre-diabetes and diabetes. For these people the blood sugar rises more quickly and to a higher level, when eating any carbohydrates, even the better high-fibre carbs. They should ideally get into the habit of being aware of the carbohydrate content of different foods or checking labels. Cutting down on high carbohydrate foods like bread will help them to lose weight and be healthier. You may not know if you are in this group, but a blood test every 2-3 years to check for pre-diabetes or raised triglyceride fats would help. After trying a low carb diet, if you do not reach your weight loss goal, you may progress to a very low carb diet such as the New Atkins or Keto, ideally with the support of a dietician.

PREBIOTICS & PROBIOTICS

A diverse community of gut bacteria is important for a healthy weight and in influencing the amount of calories that your body absorbs. See also page 272.

SMALL PLATES

The great Jewish physician and philosopher, Maimonides (the Rambam) advised that we stop eating when we are three-quarters full. We tend to overeat and overdrink when given large portions on huge plates or in big beakers. Takeaways and fast food outlets often serve over-sized portions particularly of carbs such as rice, pasta or chips, another reason to cook at home.

It is possible to trick the brain into eating less by using smaller plates, starting the meal with a soup or a salad, portioning out the food at the start of the meal, removing the serving dish from the table, and filling your plate with protein and vegetables, leaving less room for white carbs. If you have made more than needed, putting the extra into freezable containers before you even sit down to eat can help. Avoid the temptation to go back for seconds or finish off the leftovers so you can "wash the pot."

SLEEP

If possible, try not to eat your last meal of the day within three hours of going to bed. The food will not be fully digested, and is more likely to be laid down as fat. When over-tired, we're more likely to be impulsive and over-eat, so aim to get seven to eight hours of sleep a night if you can. Some foods can help you get to sleep by stimulating melatonin, the hormone that regulates sleep. These include walnuts, sour cherries, and bananas. Caffeine and alcohol have the opposite effect.

EXERCISE & VISCERAL FAT

Regular vigorous exercise is important for reducing the risk of diabetes. It also has the most impact on reducing the amount of fat around your midriff and internal organs, known as visceral fat. When body fat is laid down, it is stored under the skin but also around the internal organs, including the heart, pancreas, and liver. It is visible around your middle as a spare tyre, or more accurately, an inner tube.

Visceral fat may damage the organs and interfere with their function, bringing an increased risk of heart disease, diabetes and liver disease. On the other hand, being generally chubby, with the fat mostly around the hips and thighs and under the surface of the skin, carries less risk.

Research by Professor Iris Shai indicates that large amounts of visceral fat can cause inflammation, which may also link to illnesses such as heart disease or cancer. Women should aim for a waistline of less than 80 cm (31.5") and men for less than 94 cm (37"). If your waistline is larger, you probably need to reduce it.

When people lament that they have been exercising regularly without seeing their weight go down, it is likely that their waistline is in fact reducing, the key to long term health. If they continue to exercise and eat healthily, weight loss should follow.

WEIGHT LOSS STRATEGIES

* Follow a Mediterranean diet

* Try intermittent fasting or time-restricted eating

* Try a low carb diet, especially if you are diabetic

* Fasting diets and low carb diets are not suitable for children

* Follow Maimonides' advice and stop eating when you are three-quarters full

* Eat more fibre

* Eat prebiotic and probiotic foods to feed your good gut bacteria

* Minimise sugar and avoid sugary drinks

* Cut out bread, including bagels

* Eat extra protein to help keep weight off without losing muscle mass

* Take regular exercise to reduce your waistline

* Prioritise sleep

A HEALTHY BLOOD PRESSURE

To understand how blood pressure works, imagine blowing into two different balloons. The first is made of a stretchy elastic material and expands as you blow into it, with little pressure being exerted on the internal walls. The second balloon has thicker, less stretchy walls so you have to blow really hard to inflate it. The air pressure in this balloon is higher, since it took more puff to blow it up. Similarly, when you are young, your blood vessels are more elastic and flexible and your blood pressure is lower. As you get older, the walls of the blood vessels tend to become stiffer and less flexible, but the same volume of blood still has to pass through them. This creates more pressure and leads to high blood pressure, known as hypertension.

HAVE YOUR BLOOD PRESSURE CHECKED

While high blood pressure is more common over the age of 50, it can also affect younger adults, especially pregnant women. Usually, there is nothing to warn you that your blood pressure has gone up. Some people notice headaches, but this is not common. It's a good idea for the practice nurse to check your blood pressure once or twice a year, more often if it is high. Diagnosing elevated blood pressure early can make a big difference. Careful treatment and monitoring can prevent strain to the heart and kidneys, and reduce the risk of a heart attack or stroke.

Treatment for high blood pressure usually combines diet, exercise, and sometimes medication. It is important to cut down on salt and gradually lose weight if you are overweight. Foods that help to open the blood vessels and improve circulation and blood pressure include beetroot, lettuce, spinach, rocket, celery, Swiss chard, nuts, citrus fruits, and in moderation, dark 70-80% cocoa chocolate. Regular exercise is important but should not be strenuous if your blood pressure is very high.

SALT

Excess salt reduces the kidneys' ability to remove water from the body by drawing it into the blood vessels and raising blood pressure. It is essential to minimise salt for babies and young children whose kidneys are not fully developed, as well as for the elderly and people suffering from kidney disease or diabetes.

You should not consume more than 6 g (1 teaspoon) of salt per day. Start by cutting out salty snacks and "nosh" such as crisps, salted nuts, and other packet snacks, and try not to add table salt to your meals. Eating more fresh food and less processed food is the safest way to be sure of what you are eating. Processed cheese, often used in pizzas, and processed or deli meat tend to be particularly high in salt. Crackers may be salted to enhance their flavour. Even some non-alcoholic drinks, such as cola, have added salt. Manufacturers add this together with caffeine. They make you thirsty and more likely to drink more.

Stock cubes, soy sauce and many bought soups and sauces can be high in salt, although sometimes lower-salt versions are available. You can also make your own broth or stock (see page 47). When you cook fresh food, you can replace some of the salt with herbs, spices, garlic, or extra pepper. Your food will still be tasty and you will soon find that your taste changes and that you no longer want to eat salty food.

MAGNESIUM

Magnesium is also good for your blood pressure and can be found in soya, pumpkin seeds, Swiss chard, spinach, eggs, nuts, and halibut amongst other foods. It works by dilating the blood vessels and so helping to improve blood flow.

SUGAR & ALCOHOL

Cutting down on sugar is crucial and will help you to lose weight, also helping your blood pressure. One of the main reasons for stiffening of the blood vessels is the repeated raising of your blood sugar. It can damage protein molecules in the blood vessels' lining. Another cause is an excess of saturated fat.

More than one in six cases of raised blood pressure are due to drinking too much alcohol. By cutting down alcohol, there can be a gradual improvement. It's wise to stay within the recommended limit of 14 units of alcohol a week. That's roughly one small glass of wine a day.

CARBS

Reducing all starchy foods while continuing to have a good amount of fruit and vegetables has been shown to help blood pressure control. Most people who follow a low carb diet and have a history of raised blood pressure find that they can reduce their blood pressure medication with the support of their doctor. See also page 258.

POTASSIUM

Increasing potassium in your diet, by eating more bananas and tomatoes, for example, helps lower blood pressure. Potassium balances the sodium in your body. Other foods with good levels of potassium include: avocados, spinach, sweet potatoes, grapes, melons, dates, and dried apricots. Some people use Lo-Salt, which is a potassium-rich alternative to table salt, but do discuss this with your doctor if you are on any blood pressure medication or have kidney problems, as excess potassium can be harmful, especially when taken with certain medications.

FRUIT & VEGETABLES

Fruit and vegetables containing the antioxidant quercetin help to reduce blood pressure. These include apples, onions, and cherries. Garlic is also protective and helps to reduce blood clotting, so is good for heart health. Some grains, including buckwheat and quinoa, have been noted to help bring blood pressure down.

OTHER FOODS

Milk contains a protein that acts like a low dose of a widely used blood pressure treatment called an ACE Inhibitor. Taking dairy products in moderation on a regular basis may help control your blood pressure. Indeed the DASH diet for people with raised blood pressure includes dairy products. The calcium in milk may also be helpful. Whole grains and canned fish, such as sardines, are also a good source of calcium.

DASH – THE DIET FOR PEOPLE
WITH RAISED BLOOD PRESSURE

Research by the Dietary Approaches to Stopping Hypertension group, or DASH, has shown that a healthy diet with plenty of fruit, vegetables, chicken, fish, nuts and whole grains, while cutting down on fat and sugar, and sugar-sweetened drinks, helps to reduce blood pressure. The effect of this diet is helped by having less salt and by having foods rich in potassium, magnesium, calcium, and fibre. It is quite similar to the Mediterranean diet but puts more emphasis on certain vegetables, seeds, and low salt.

The DASH diet can lower blood pressure almost as effectively as a low dose of medication but only if you stick to it, so it is best taken on with the support and guidance of a dietician. If you are already on blood pressure pills, the DASH diet will boost the effect of the medication, but do not stop taking medication without first consulting your doctor.

IN A NUTSHELL

The most important way to control your blood pressure is maintaining a healthy weight and reducing your intake of salt, sugar, and alcohol. If your doctor has prescribed tablets to treat raised blood pressure, it is important to take these regularly, and they should only be stopped if you are told it is safe to do so. A healthy diet goes hand in hand with blood pressure medication.

HEALTHY BLOOD PRESSURE

* Hypertension typically has no symptoms, so regular check-ups are important

* Cutting down salt, alcohol, and losing weight are key to lowering blood pressure

* Reducing sugar and saturated fat can make your blood vessels more flexible

* Potassium, magnesium, and calcium help lower blood pressure

* Tomatoes, grapes, and bananas are good potassium sources

* Pumpkin seeds, whole grains, and chard are good sources of magnesium

* Dairy products, dark green leafy vegetables, and whole grains are good sources of calcium

* Beetroot can lower blood pressure by opening up the blood vessels

* A low carb diet can reduce the need for hypertension medication

* The DASH diet may be effective to reduce blood pressure and lose weight

* Exercise, but don't overdo it.

A HEALTHY HEART

Diet can significantly reduce the risk of coronary heart disease. Positive steps include eating a traditional Mediterranean diet, more fibre, plenty of fruit and vegetables, including beetroot, nuts, good fats and fermented foods while cutting down on sugar, white carbs, saturated fats, alcohol and salt.

One of the world's longest-running nutrition studies, the Predimed Study (Prevención con Dieta Mediterránea) has shown that the Mediterranean diet reduces the risk of heart disease by about 30% and also improves longevity. The Israeli kibbutz style diet is close to the traditional Mediterranean diet, and one of the healthiest diets in the world.

Risk factors for developing heart disease are linked to one another and include diabetes, raised cholesterol, hypertension, and being overweight. Diabetes alone is known to increase the risk of heart disease by 100% to 500%. Dietary changes can reduce most of these risk factors and can influence more than one factor at the same time. For example, losing weight lowers both blood pressure and the risk of diabetes.

In my experience as a doctor, prevention is better than cure, and it is always better to try and prevent heart-related diseases from occurring in the first place, than to take action belatedly.

HEALTHY FATS

When the Predimed study assessed the individual parts of the Mediterranean diet, it revealed that nuts and extra virgin olive oil, high in antioxidants and monounsaturated fat, offer the most protection against heart disease. Seeds such as flaxseed (linseed) are also rich in heart-healthy fats, as are avocados.

Omega-3, from oily fish such as salmon, reduces several risks for heart disease – inflammation, high blood pressure, irregular heartbeat, and the level of triglycerides (a kind of fat). For some people with ischaemic heart disease and raised triglycerides, high doses of EPA, a long-chain form of omega-3, have been shown to reduce the risk of further heart attacks. Saturated fats, especially from red meat and processed meat, may raise LDL (bad) cholesterol. Replacing these with polyunsaturated fat from nuts and seeds, such as cold-pressed rapeseed oil, can also reduce the risk of heart disease.

NUTS & LEGUMES

Unsalted, unsweetened nuts are a standout part of the Mediterranean diet. They contain vitamin E, a powerful antioxidant, have a low glycaemic index, and have been shown to help lower the risk of diabetes, high blood pressure, and stroke. Nuts are also a good source of essential polyunsaturated fatty acids, minerals such as magnesium and selenium, and heart-healthy monounsaturated fat, which can help lower LDL cholesterol and raise HDL (good) cholesterol.

Nuts also contain arginine, a protein that helps open up blood vessels and improve circulation. A small handful of plain nuts is a great snack, and far healthier than eating a biscuit or a piece of cake, although do so in moderation as large quantities of nuts mean lots of calories. Do remember to ask about allergies before serving anything that contains nuts or nut oil.

The Mediterranean diet includes pulses and legumes such as beans and chickpeas. Not only are these foods cheap, they are high in protein, fibre, and B vitamins, and are excellent for heart health, which may help to explain why people living in the Mediterranean region enjoy long life.

LENTILS

FIVE-A-DAY

Most people nowadays are aware of the Five-a-Day campaign that encourages us to eat at least five portions of fruit and vegetables a day. The European Prospective Investigation into Cancer and Nutrition (EPIC) study, in which more than half a million people took part, showed that eight portions of fruit and vegetables daily cut the risk of fatal heart attacks by 22%. It is best to prioritise the vegetables over the fruit because they are lower in natural sugar. This is particularly important for smoothies where you don't want to bring on a rapid rise in blood sugar.

WHOLE GRAINS

Whole grains and fibre can help lower cholesterol levels by reducing fat absorption in the gut. Taken regularly up to 3 times daily, they can help to reduce heart disease risk by about 23%. See also page 248.

OTHER HELPFUL FOODS

Beetroot, spinach, nuts, citrus fruits, and dark chocolate all promote good circulation (see page 241). Garlic and onions help to reduce blood clots, improve blood pressure, and lower LDL cholesterol. All members of the onion family, including spring onions, shallots, and leeks are heart-healthy. If you don't like the taste of garlic, or wish to avoid garlicky breath, you can take garlic pills instead.

VITAMIN K2

This is produced in your body by good gut bacteria and eating fermented foods. It seems to reduce the calcium deposited in the coronary arteries, and may turn out to have an important role in preventing heart disease. Research on vitamin K2 is ongoing, but countries where people have low K2 levels appear to have more coronary heart disease among younger people. If you don't eat much fermented food, it is possible to buy vitamin K2 supplements, but the ideal dose is still under debate. K2 supplements should not be taken if you are on blood-thinning medications such as warfarin. See also page 234.

SUGAR & ALCOHOL

Most of us are aware that cutting down sugary foods, snacks, and sweetened drinks helps reduce the risk of diabetes, but it may also help to prevent heart disease, high blood pressure, and improve the balance between good and bad cholesterol.

Over 80% of our cholesterol is manufactured in the body. When excess sugar is eaten, it stimulates the liver to produce small dense LDL cholesterol and triglyceride fats. This small dense LDL is a form of cholesterol more likely to cause narrowing of the arteries of the heart. Sugar can also contribute towards an unpleasant and dangerous group of conditions known as the metabolic syndrome. This includes increased fat around the internal organs (visceral fat), raised LDL cholesterol, raised blood pressure, and prediabetes. People with the metabolic syndrome are at high risk of heart disease.

In her book The Big Fat Surprise, investigative journalist Nina Teicholz discovered that the people in Crete had a very low incidence of heart disease and less illness than those living in adjacent islands who also ate a Mediterranean diet. This difference was due to the combination of a Mediterranean diet and very low sugar intake. Cretans, it turned out, preferred fresh seasonal fruit rather than desserts, and ate hardly any of the sugar-laden pastries so popular elsewhere in Greece.

There is a direct link between alcohol intake and blood pressure. Reducing alcohol can not only help lower blood pressure, but also reduce obesity and the risk of heart muscle damage (cardiomyopathy). All forms of alcohol are potentially harmful when drunk in significant quantities, although a small glass of dry red wine can have some benefit to the heart due to polyphenols (antioxidants) from the grape skins.

ATRIAL FIBRILLATION (AF)

This is when the heart rhythm becomes irregular and often very rapid. Symptoms may include palpitations, dizziness, or chest pain, although many people are unaware it is happening. AF can dislodge pre-existing blood clots, which may be a risk for strokes. Following a Mediterranean diet and limiting alcohol intake may reduce the risk of AF. Atrial fibrillation can occur at a relatively young age. Blood-thinning medication (anticoagulants) can significantly lower its risks, so if you think you may have AF, seek medical attention quickly.

A HEALTHY HEART

* The Mediterranean diet is great for the heart, especially in combination with low sugar and limited white carbs

* Three portions of whole grains a day can reduce your risk of heart disease by 23%

* Unsalted nuts, beetroot, and oranges are good for the circulation

* Oily fish, avocados, nuts, seeds, and extra virgin olive oil are rich in heart-healthy monounsaturated and polyunsaturated fats

* Fermented foods boost heart-healthy vitamin K2

* Eat more vegetables than fruit, five or more portions daily

* Eat less red meat and avoid processed meat

* Only eat saturated fats like butter and cheese in moderation

* Don't eat more than 1 teaspoon of salt a day

* Avoid excess sugar

* Exercise regularly and don't smoke

A HEALTHY CHOLESTEROL LEVEL

Cholesterol is a fat needed for the production of hormones, to make cell walls, and to improve immunity. HDL cholesterol helps to reduce narrowing of blood vessel walls and may protect against heart disease, whereas LDL cholesterol can be laid down in the lining of blood vessels and is thought to be one of the main causes of heart disease. Some researchers now think the risks from high LDL cholesterol may be overstated.

SATURATED FAT

Most of our saturated fat comes from animal sources such as meat and dairy products, as well as coconut oil and palm oil. In the past, it was thought that those wanting to lower their cholesterol level should avoid foods such as eggs, butter, and meat. Current research, however, suggests that eaten in moderation these foods can be part of a healthy diet. Current UK national guidelines recommend that women should not exceed 20 grams of saturated fat daily, and men no more than 30 grams daily.

EGGS

Although rich in cholesterol, eggs do not normally raise your LDL cholesterol. Their benefits include high levels of vitamins A, D, E, and K, all good for the heart, and choline that helps protect against Alzheimer's disease. Please don't join the trend for eating only the white, because most of the good stuff is in the yolk.

BUTTER

This has a mixed reputation. Its saturated fat is more concentrated than in other forms of dairy foods. Used sparingly, I consider it a healthier choice than margarine, which is highly processed. Butter from the milk of grass-fed cows contains healthier fat than that from grain-fed animals and has more omega-3.

COCONUT OIL

Although high in saturated fat, coconut oil may benefit your metabolism, but more research is needed on the pros and cons.

HEALTHY WHOLE FOOD SPREADS

If your LDL cholesterol is significantly raised, it is best to avoid or minimise butter. Chickpeas and sesame seeds help lower LDL cholesterol, so spread hummus or tahini on your toast instead of butter or margarine. Spreading some ripe avocado on oatcakes or dipping wholemeal toast in a little extra virgin olive oil are also great alternatives.

WHOLE GRAINS & NUTS

Whole grains, beans and lentils and plain unsalted nuts can lower LDL cholesterol. Oats are particularly effective at reducing cholesterol in the bloodstream. A bowl of porridge is a great way to start the day, using berries for sweetness rather than syrup or honey. Low salt sugar-free nut butters are rich in monounsaturated fat and make good spreads. It's easy to make your own by grinding whole unsalted nuts in a food processor or blender.

OMEGA-3

Omega-3 and monounsaturated fats tend to raise HDL (High-Density Lipoprotein), while omega-6 fats lower LDL (Low-Density Lipoprotein). All these fats are best taken by eating whole foods, particularly oily fish, nuts, seeds such as flaxseed (linseed) and chia, and avocados. Extra virgin olive oil, which is high in monounsaturated fat, is also protective.

OMEGA-6

Omega-6 is a type of polyunsaturated fat found in soya, nuts, and seeds, as well as meat, eggs, and dairy products. It is also found in seed-based oils such as sunflower and in groundnut and soya oil. Like all polyunsaturated fats, it can help lower LDL cholesterol. Eaten in whole foods such as nuts and seeds and in dairy products, from grass-fed animals, it is healthier than that in refined oil and margarine.

Omega-3 and omega-6 compete for the same enzymes in the body, so excess omega-6 can reduce the benefits of the omega-3. The ideal ratio of omega-6 to omega-3 in our diet is under debate. Some researchers suggest a ratio of about 4:1 or less, though most of us average closer to 16:1. You can reduce the amount of omega-6 in your diet by switching from sunflower to cold-pressed rapeseed oil, for example. Alternatively, eating more oily fish will redress the balance and allow the omega-3 to do its work.

POULTRY

Fresh chicken and turkey have a limited effect on LDL cholesterol. Processed chicken in factory-made sausages will have similar health risks to other processed meats.

RED MEAT

Red meat has saturated fat but is also high in protein, iron, zinc, and B vitamins. A very high intake of red meat can lead to an increase in small dense LDL cholesterol, (the most harmful form). We should ideally reduce the quantity of red meat taken in our diet and replace it with other proteins such as fish and nuts.

PLANT STEROLS & STANOLS

Some plants contain natural substances that can help to lower LDL ("bad") cholesterol and are added to "cholesterol-lowering" spreads. However, they may reduce the absorption of some vitamins and are not currently recommended by the UK National Institute for Health and Care Excellence (NICE)

SOYA

Soya beans contain isoflavones which have been proven to lower LDL cholesterol and may reduce the risk of heart disease. In small quantities, soy-based foods such as tofu may be a good alternative to red meat, and tempeh, a fermented form of soya, is good for your gut bacteria. However, soy crops are often genetically modified, with as yet unknown side effects, and many soy food products such as vegetarian schnitzels are highly processed and contain large amounts of salt.

SUGAR & WHITE CARBS

To avoid high LDL cholesterol, cut down on sugary drinks, and snacks, fruit juices and desserts. Some of the fructose in sugar converts in the liver to small dense LDL, the form most damaging to the heart. White carbs such as bread and pasta raise other fats called triglycerides, also a risk to the heart.

A low carb diet can improve the balance between good and bad cholesterol, enabling people to reduce their medications, such as statins. However, it is important to discuss this with the doctor first.

TRANS FATS

Trans fats, which are sometimes labelled Partially Hydrogenated Fats, increase the levels of "bad" LDL. Trans fats are very unhealthy for your heart, and were once widely used in processed foods, especially in dairy-free and parev products. Fortunately, they have almost completely been removed from UK and US food supplies. It is worth checking the label on shop-bought cakes, pies, and pastries, however, especially if they are imported. Traces of trans fats may be formed when omega-6 fats, such as sunflower oil are re-used for deep frying.

PROCESSED FOODS

Processed snacks tend to raise your LDL cholesterol. Factory-made pies, pastries and crisps as well as deli meats such as pastrami or salami are often made with large quantities of refined fats and are not a healthy choice, even if they look lean.

IF YOU DO HAVE HIGH CHOLESTEROL

A diet low in white carbs and high in vegetables, fibre, especially from oats, legumes, and pulses and healthy fats from whole foods like fish, nuts, and seeds, can significantly improve your cholesterol profile. Reduce fried foods, packaged snacks, pastries, sugar, red meat, and processed meat. Choose skimmed or semi-skimmed milk rather than whole, and eat butter and cheese only in moderation.

Ashkenazi Jews are at higher risk of a condition called familial hypercholesterolaemia (FH) than the general population. This is an inherited type of high cholesterol, which, fortunately is rare If you have very high cholesterol, or members of your extended family have had unusually high LDL cholesterol or heart attacks at an early age, it is wise to discuss the subject with your doctor.

If you are diagnosed with FH, it is likely you will need medication and a diet very low in saturated fat and cholesterol. Do everything you can to lower your cholesterol, and cut down on saturated fats such as butter, chicken fat and red meat.

HEALTHY CHOLESTEROL

* Eat plenty of fish, nuts, seeds, avocados, and extra virgin olive oil

* Choose pulses legumes and whole grains, especially oats

* Cutting down sugar reduces the most harmful form of LDL cholesterol

* Use spreads such as hummus, tahini, and nut butters

* Butter is OK but use it sparingly

* Eggs don't usually raise cholesterol

* Omega-6 fats, including sunflower oil, may compete with omega-3 so try to hit the right balance

* Cut down on sugar, cakes and pastries, refined or highly processed oils, and margarine

* Avoid processed foods including crisps, pretzels, sausages, and deli meats

* Take all saturated fats in moderation

* If you have familial hyper-cholesterolaemia, be especially cautious about saturated fats

A HEALTHY BRAIN

Even if one or both of your parents have suffered from dementia, the good news is that this is not inevitably your destiny too. Although genes do play a part, there is plenty you can do to reduce your risk.

There are two main types of dementia: vascular dementia and Alzheimer's disease. Vascular dementia is due to narrowed blood vessels and blood clots, which cause repeated strokes. For more on risk factors for stroke see pages 241-251.

Minor strokes sometimes have such mild symptoms that they are mistaken for dizziness or "a funny turn". Over time, they can cause confusion and memory loss.

Alzheimer's disease is less well understood, but it often begins at a younger age and the onset is more gradual.

PREVENTING VASCULAR DEMENTIA

Healthy circulation is key to reducing the risk of vascular dementia. All the strategies I recommend for a healthy heart, blood pressure, and cholesterol level are vital for preventing vascular dementia. Hand in hand with a good diet, it is also important to keep to a healthy weight, not smoke, and exercise regularly, ideally for more than an hour and a half each week.

THE "MIND" DIET

The Mediterranean diet is good for reducing heart disease, and the DASH diet for reducing blood pressure. They have been combined as the MIND Diet, which helps prevent both vascular dementia and Alzheimer's disease. Like the Mediterranean diet, it does not involve calorie counting and is a long-term lifestyle for good health.

THE "MIND" DIET

EVERY DAY

* Mixed vegetables, including dark green leafy vegetables

* Whole grains with every meal

* Nuts and berries

* Salad with lashings of olive oil

* A small glass of red wine or low sugar grape juice

SEVERAL TIMES A WEEK

* Fish and chicken

* Beans of any kind

* Turmeric in drinks, stews or curries

NO-GOS

* Limit red meat

* Minimise sugar, salt, and margarine

* Eat less butter

* Fry very rarely

* Avoid "nosh" and pastries

AVOIDING DEMENTIA

Leonard and Betty are inseparable. They have various aches and pains, but consider themselves lucky they are still living independently in their own home. Their parents had not been so fortunate, suffering ill health in their later years.

There was a time when Betty baked regularly. Her cakes were legendary, and every meal ended with dessert. When they reached middle age, however, they decided it was time to change the way they ate. Lunch was usually salmon and salad, fruit replaced puddings, and baking was saved for special occasions. Evening meals were more varied, but always using fresh ingredients.

They had both always been slim, so the results of their change in diet at first were not obvious. As time passed, however, they started to notice the benefit of continuing health and intellectual agility. Their daily game of Rummikub is testament to this.

When it comes to our genes and family histories, we are all dealt a different hand, but a healthy lifestyle and the right diet can make a difference to the final outcome.

PREVENTING ALZHEIMER'S DISEASE

Controlling your blood sugar, antioxidant-rich foods, reducing inflammation, feeding your good gut bacteria, and promoting neurogenesis (the growth of new brain cells) all help reduce the risk of developing Alzheimer's disease. Regular exercise and brain training – solving puzzles, crosswords, or sudoku – can also help.

CONTROLLING BLOOD SUGAR & INSULIN

Researchers have noticed that a persistently high insulin level, found in badly controlled type-2 diabetes, is associated with Alzheimer's disease, and now believe the two diseases may be related. Some even refer to Alzheimer's as type-3 diabetes. Preventing or reversing diabetes may therefore reduce the risk of Alzheimer's. If you do have diabetes, good control through diet and medication can help reduce the risk. See also page 258.

ANTIOXIDANTS, VITAMINS & MINERALS

Antioxidant-rich food and drinks, such as green tea and blueberries, improve brain function (see page 223). Vitamin D from sunlight exposure, and vitamin E from healthy fats can improve memory and learning. Zinc, magnesium, and manganese, from nuts, whole grains, and seeds such as flaxseed and pumpkin seeds, also help brain function by supporting enzyme production.

GUT BACTERIA & VITAMINS

There is emerging evidence that supporting good gut bacteria through diet reduces the risk of dementia, possibly via a chemical link between the gut and brain known as the gut-brain axis. Gut bacteria produce B vitamins, folic acid, and biotin, all important for brain function. Vitamin K2 from fermented foods also appears to support brain health. See also page 234.

BOOSTING NEUROTRANSMITTERS

Neurotransmitters are chemicals that pass messages between neurons (nerve cells). Choline is a nutrient that helps in the production of an essential neurotransmitter (acetylcholine). Eggs, cod, salmon, and liver are good sources. Smaller amounts of choline are in broccoli, cauliflower, sunflower seeds, and in lecithin supplements.

Herbs such as sage and ginseng may help the production of neurotransmitters. Ginkgo biloba has a reputation for improving memory. Even basil and parsley may have benefits. However, studies on herbal treatments for dementia are not conclusive. If you are considering a herbal supplement, discuss it with your doctor, and do not discontinue prescription medication without consulting them.

OMEGA-3

Dr Alex Richardson, a leading expert on fatty acids, has observed that omega-3 is critical for normal brain structure and function. Over 60% of the brain is fat, so the composition of this fat is important. Fish such as salmon, fish oils, and algae oils are the best sources, as very little omega-3 from other vegetarian foods ever reaches the brain.

The active forms of omega-3, EPA and DHA, make nerve cell membranes less rigid and help with the transmission of messages between cells. The greatest benefit of omega-3 for brain health comes from taking it to prevent rather than to treat Alzheimer's disease, so take it all your life. Since omega-3 and omega-6 compete for the same enzymes, it's best to use omega-6-rich oils, such as sunflower, in moderation, and use cold-pressed rather than refined forms.

WATER

Staying hydrated is important for brain health and concentration. Drinking six to eight glasses of water a day is recommended.

INFLAMMATION

Inflammation occurs when the immune system is overworked, causing tissue damage, often through the release of chemicals. Foods such as extra virgin olive oil and certain herbs and spices, help calm inflammation, reducing the risk of chronic illnesses including Alzheimer's disease. Others, especially highly processed foods, can increase inflammation (see page 273).

NEUROGENESIS

Adult neurogenesis is the formation of new brain cells, or neurons, throughout adult life. Key research in this area has been by Dr Sandrine Thuret, a neuroscientist at King's College, London, showing that even though brain cells die as we age, new ones can still be created. This happens mostly in the hippocampus, the part of the brain responsible for memory, so neurogenesis is important to help preserve the intellect.

Dr Thuret discovered that intermittent fasting, be it time-restricted eating, the 2-day or 5:2 diet, or a keto diet, benefits neurogenesis. Although not suitable for everyone, fasting improves the action of the newly discovered Klotho gene that helps reduce the signs of ageing (see page 260.) Dr Thuret also found that regular exercise increases new nerve cell growth.

OTHER NEUROGENESIS BOOSTERS

Antioxidants, found in purple fruit, dark chocolate, and green tea also help neurogenesis. Flavonoids, a type of antioxidant, have also been shown to boost neurogenesis. Extracts of blueberries were used in these studies, it was concluded that other antioxidants should offer the same benefit.

Folic acid, a type of B vitamin found in green leafy vegetables, has been found to increase production of new nerve cells by reducing levels of a harmful chemical called homocysteine. Turmeric contains circumin, a chemical with antioxidant properties, which also appears to lower the risk of Alzheimer's disease by boosting neurogenesis and reducing inflammation. In one study, four weeks after regularly taking turmeric, patients were less anxious and demonstrated improved memory. See also page 235.

WHAT INHIBITS NEUROGENESIS?

Alcohol is toxic to the brain and washes out omega-3, so inhibiting neurogenesis. A study from Oxford University following five hundred middle-aged adults over thirty years, found that alcohol caused shrinkage of the right hippocampus and loss of neurons on MRI scans. The more alcohol consumed, the worse it was. Other studies have shown benefits to the brain from small amounts of red wine, which is why it is included in the MIND Diet.

Sugar appears to inhibit neurogenesis, possibly through the action of insulin, or perhaps because it promotes inflammation. Eating soft foods has also been found to limit neurogenesis; it appears that the act of chewing increases blood supply to the brain. Not surprisingly, sleep deprivation and stress are also bad for neurogenesis.

LOOKING AHEAD

Regular exercise, brain training, and a healthy diet can all help reduce the risk of dementia. Doctors in the USA are now combining these lifestyle changes, time-restricted eating, herbs, and medications to treat early Alzheimer's disease, with some success. This method is in its infancy and research is ongoing. Some memory loss is a normal part of ageing. However, if you are concerned about dementia, do talk to your doctor. An early diagnosis can improve the outcome and quality of life.

STRATEGIES FOR A HEALTHY BRAIN

* Eat healthy fats including omega-3 and extra virgin olive oil

* Eat foods rich in choline, such as eggs, cod, salmon, sunflower seeds, and lecithin

* Vitamin E, found in nuts, seeds, olive oil, and avocados, helps protect the brain

* Oily fish, fruit, especially berries, vegetables, and turmeric aid neurogenesis, the formation of new brain cells

* Intermittent fasting, sleep, regular exercise, and "brain training" support brain health

* Alcohol, sugar, and highly processed food inhibit neurogenesis

* Strategies for a healthy heart are also good for a healthy brain

TYPE 2 DIABETES

The simplest way to reduce your risk of developing type 2 diabetes is to eat as though you have diabetes, though less strictly. Changes in diet and lifestyle can reverse pre-diabetes, and we now know that some people with established type 2 diabetes can reverse their condition, but prevention is easier.

CUT CARBS & MINIMISE SUGAR

Cutting down sugar intake is a cornerstone of diabetes prevention and treatment. To lower your risk, minimise sugar in hot drinks, fruit juice and fizzy drinks. A single 330 ml can of standard cola contains almost nine teaspoons of sugar! Health and nutrition writer Jane E Brody noted in the New York Times that, "the average adult would have to walk about two miles to work off the effects of a 16 oz soda (at which point the walker might be inclined to down another soda)." Regularly drinking just a couple of sugar-sweetened drinks daily increases your risk of diabetes by 26%.

MINIMISE ALCOHOL

It is important to limit alcohol intake because of its high sugar content (especially in sweet wines such as Kiddush wine or cocktails made with sugary mixers) in addition to the harmful effects of the alcohol itself. "Light" wines and reduced-sugar juice are better alternatives than grape juice, which is also high in sugar. Both can be watered down or sipped in small quantities. Beer is lower in sugar than wine and spirits but high in carbohydrates, so is sometimes referred to as 'liquid toast'.

NOSH ON NUTS

Plain nuts can help in diabetes prevention and are an ideal snack if you are not allergic. Although relatively high in calories, nuts contain healthy fats and have a low glycaemic index. Eaten in moderation, just a small palmful at a time, they can help you lose weight and reduce your waistline.

EAT EXTRA FIBRE

When it comes to diabetes prevention, fibre excels, especially the lower carbohydrate forms such as flax seeds and nuts. Legumes, including peas, beans, lentils, chickpeas and soya beans, can also help reduce the risk of diabetes. This effect is probably due to their high fibre content and their positive impact on the microbiome. Having porridge or bran cereal for breakfast is another good source of fibre, as is eating fresh fruit and vegetables with the skin on.

REDUCE WHITE CARBS & STARCHY FOODS

Highly refined grains, such as white rice, white flour, matzah, matzah meal and white pasta are not so good for your health, especially for people who have either pre-diabetes or diabetes. They break down quickly to sugar, giving a spike in the blood levels of glucose and insulin.

Root vegetables, such as potatoes and parsnips, are high in starch, which is converted to glucose by your digestion. Carrots have a lower starch content and have less impact on the blood sugar when eaten raw. Legumes are also starchy, but they have benefits noted above; those eaten with the pod, such as green beans and mangetout, are better for your blood sugar. Leafy vegetables tend to be low in starch and are favoured by dieticians.

GO LOW CARB

To reduce the risk of diabetes, cut down on all carbohydrates, especially white carbs. Eat smaller portions of whole grains and starchy vegetables, but do not fully exclude them from your diet. This is a balancing act – you need fibre and nutrients while staying low carb, especially if you are pre-diabetic or diabetic. Nuts, lentils, and quinoa are sources of fibre that are relatively high in protein and lower in carbohydrates. A useful technique is to eat one meal a day that is very low in carbs but also contains vegetables or fruit. This can progress to reducing carbohydrates in all your meals. Books or apps that show suitable portion sizes for brown bread, wholegrain rice, and pasta can also be helpful.

GO MEAT FREE?

Studies have shown that eating less red meat and processed meat reduces the risk of diabetes. It can be challenging to cut back on meat when following a low carbohydrate diet. Substitute other types of protein, such as fish, soya, nuts, and eggs.

FRUIT & VEGETABLES

Quercetin, an antioxidant found in apples, onions and citrus fruits, gives extra protection against diabetes. Apples and pears, although relatively low in carbs, are also high in pectin, a soluble fibre, which can be helpful. Berries, particularly blueberries, are packed with antioxidants, have a low glycaemic index, and can reduce the risk of developing diabetes.

If you have prediabetes or diabetes, it's important to know which fruits are particularly high in natural sugars. These include sultanas, raisins, dates, and pineapple, and grapes. Some people with diabetes are particularly sensitive to sweet fruits and should try to exclude them from their diet, although they can be eaten occasionally, especially with nuts.

DAIRY FOOD & EGGS

Dairy products lower the risk of diabetes. Full-fat unsweetened Greek natural yoghurt is high in protein and eaten with berries or other fruit, nuts or seeds makes a satisfying dessert. Diabetes UK says that eggs are not a risk factor for diabetes. They can help to prevent weight gain and are rich in nutrients, including vitamin D. For most people, the cholesterol in egg yolks does not raise their blood LDL cholesterol.

DRINK LOTS OF WATER

Water is essential for a normal metabolism. If blood sugars are high, it prevents dehydration and helps the kidneys to flush out sugar. It's calorie-free, so is the ideal drink, and we aim to have about eight glasses a day.

EXERCISE REGULARLY

If you can combine the above advice with regular physical activity, the risk of going downhill from prediabetes to full diabetes is cut by 58%. For people who are not used to exercise, it is important to build this up gradually such as by walking regularly and taking hourly breaks to move around if they have a sedentary job

LOSE SOME WEIGHT — AND KEEP IT OFF

One of the greatest risk factors for type 2 diabetes is being overweight. Losing weight and maintaining this weight-loss can be an effective way of preventing diabetes. Try to drop 5% off your weight if you are at risk. Recent research has shown that weight loss of around 15 kg can often reverse diabetes, especially if initiated soon after diagnosis. This removes fat from around the liver and pancreas and restores good function. A strict diet, such as going very low carb, may be needed to achieve this. See also page 237.

SPECIAL DIETS & TIME-RESTRICTED EATING

For some people, a very low carbohydrate diet can make it easier to lose weight and belly fat. One example is the modern version of the Atkins diet, also known as a keto diet. It seems that when dramatically lowering carbohydrates and burning fat for energy, people experience less hunger, fewer cravings for sweet foods, and improved blood pressure, blood sugar, and cholesterol levels. Ideally, this sort of restrictive diet should be followed with the support of a dietician or doctor. It is not suitable for pregnant women or people with kidney disease, while those on thyroid treatment may need extra monitoring.

A diet that includes short mini-fasts or time-restricted eating can be very effective, and sometimes reverse established diabetes. Although the 5:2 Diet and the 8 Week Blood Sugar Diet are the best known, the Two-Day Diet (the original intermittent fasting diet) is also well suited to diabetes prevention because on fasting days the focus is on reducing calories and carbs.

With time-restricted eating, you avoid eating for three hours before going to sleep, and delay breakfast until 12-14 hours after the evening meal. This type of diet does not suit everyone, especially if on certain medications, or during pregnancy. Talk to your doctor before starting this sort of regimen.

FAMILY SUPPORT

Unfortunately, even with their best effort, some people will still develop type 2 diabetes. When this happens, they should not feel guilty, but tighten up on a healthy diet while strictly cutting down on sugar. This is crucial to reduce the risk of complications such as heart disease, kidney disease, and eye damage. Regular meetings with a dietician, both for the patient and the immediate family, have been shown to improve diabetic control, and have the added benefit of helping the whole family become healthier.

TO HELP AVOID OR REVERSE PRE-DIABETES & DIABETES

* Minimise sugar and white carbs

* Eat plenty of vegetables and fruits, especially apples, pears, and berries

* Snack on unsalted, unsweetened nuts

* Squeeze out the white carbs on your plate with more protein and vegetables

* Eat one or two low carb meals a day, or go fully low carb

* Eat plenty of fibre

* Drink more water

* Drink milk

* Drink tea or coffee without sugar, and avoid sodas and other sweetened drinks

* Reduce fruit juices

* Eat less red meat, and avoid processed meat

* Try intermittent fasting with medical advice

* Exercise regularly

CASE STUDY

REVERSING PREDIABETES

Jonathan is a singer in a choir. His body had always been less than perfect, and his belly used to precede him into a room. More worryingly, he had back pain and pre-diabetes. He knew that he had good willpower, however, having successfully dieted as a young man.

He was contacted by his local surgery, which offered him the option of an NHS "Take Control" course. This included advice and inspirational presentations by a nutritionist who motivated him to change his diet and lifestyle. He cut down bread, limited the amount of alcohol he drank, and gave up milk chocolate, crisps, and most desserts. If offered them, he learned to put up his hand, palm out like a stop sign, and to ask for a cup of tea instead.

He started walking briskly three or four times a week. From there, he progressed to a gym and exercise programme, also through the NHS, that included regular weigh-ins and blood checks to monitor his progress.

Eventually, his belly slimmed down, the back pain was gone, and his blood sugar normalised. It wasn't all plain sailing, but with the right motivation and support, he has been able to achieve his goal.

KEEPING CANCER AT BAY

According to the World Cancer Research Fund, a third of all cancer cases might be prevented through a healthy diet, regular exercise and staying slim. Avoiding smoking is crucial. However, cancer has several causes, including one's genes and environment so people who get cancer should not blame themselves, as there is often little they could have done differently to prevent it.

WEIGHT CONTROL

The most detailed research is held in the Continuous Update Project of the World Cancer Research Fund. It shows that avoiding being overweight is one of the best ways to prevent cancer. Obesity is a risk for fourteen different cancers, including breast and bowel cancer. For more on weight loss see page 237.

INTERMITTENT FASTING

The Two-Day Diet is a form of intermittent fasting, developed by Professor Tony Howell and Dr Michelle Harvie of the Prevent Breast Cancer Unit at Wythenshawe Hospital in Manchester. They found that as your body ages it may build up elderly cells, known as senescent cells. These produce chemicals that damage other cells increasing the risk of cancer. Fasting helps to "mop" these up. It also helps you to lose weight, again lowering cancer risk. Intermittent fasting can also be helpful if you are being treated for cancer or are a cancer survivor, but only do so in consultation with your oncologist.

EXERCISE

Regular exercise can significantly help reduce the risk of cancer developing or returning. If you are undergoing cancer treatment, this may not be possible, however, you may be able to gradually increase your level of activity, ideally with the help of a physiotherapist.

ANTIOXIDANTS & VITAMINS

Antioxidants, including vitamins A, C, E, and selenium, can help prevent cancer by mopping up free radicals, unstable molecules that occur naturally in the body, but can be increased in number by carcinogens like cigarette smoke. When out of balance, free radicals can damage the DNA in cells, which may be the first stage in the development of cancer.

Antioxidants occur naturally in the body but can be boosted by eating certain foods which support the body's own antioxidant defences. This works more effectively than taking antioxidants in the form of tablets or supplements. However, if you are unable to eat a normal diet, it is wise to seek advice from a dietician to see if a supplement would be helpful.

Some antioxidants are fat-soluble, so eating vegetables such as beetroot, kale and spinach with a dressing made with extra virgin olive oil can enhance their antioxidant effect. Cider vinegar or red wine vinegar, fresh herbs, particularly thyme, marjoram, and lemongrass, and spices such as cumin or fresh ginger have a similar effect. Garlic may also help reduce the risk of bowel cancer. See also page 223.

CRUCIFEROUS PLANTS & VEGETABLES

Cruciferous vegetables, which include broccoli, kale, cauliflower, watercress, mustard, rocket, and radishes, help reduce the risk for several types of cancer.

FIBRE AND WHOLE GRAINS

Dietary fibre helps to prevent cancer, especially of the bowel and breast. It has been shown that three portions of whole grains daily can reduce the risk of cancer by 20%.

VITAMIN D

Vitamin D appears to help prevent cancer, especially breast and bowel cancer. Vitamin D is produced in our skin by the action of sunlight. This might explain higher levels of cancer in the less sunny northern than southern United States. See also page 234.

FAT

Cancer prevention dieticians recommend extra virgin olive oil. Omega-3 fatty acids, such as from oily fish, are also helpful. You are aiming for a higher ratio of omega-3 to omega-6 fats, helped by switching from refined seed oils, including sunflower oil, to cold-pressed rapeseed and extra virgin olive oils. Omega-3 fatty acids may help reduce the risk of lung cancer in smokers, but smoking is like playing Russian roulette with your health, so to reduce your risk of cancer stop smoking.

Avoid deep-frying, and for stir fries only use fat which has a high smoke point such as coconut oil. This avoids the production of aldehydes, chemicals known to be potentially carcinogenic. For more on cooking oil and fats, see page 232.

A VEGETARIAN DIET

Over-eating red meat appears to increase the risk of bowel cancer. Processed meat is now considered a carcinogen by the World Cancer Research Fund. Meat-free diets, especially if these include fish, offer some protection against cancer. Vegans have a 19% overall reduced risk, perhaps in part due to a generally healthy lifestyle. However, a strictly vegan diet can lead to deficiencies in calcium, omega-3, vitamin B12, and vitamin D. (see page 234).

DAIRY PRODUCTS

Milk and dairy products probably offer protection against bowel cancer through the actions of butyrate and vitamin D. However, dairy products may cause a small increase in the risk of prostate cancer.

RISK FACTORS

SUGAR & WHITE CARBS

Eating sugar-laden foods and white carbs may increase the risk of cancer. It appears that by raising insulin levels, they may promote the growth of cancer cells. People with diabetes tend to have an increased risk of getting cancer, but if they look after their diabetes and control their blood sugar, the risk is lowered.

EXCESS SALT

The risk of stomach cancer in particular can be reduced by cutting down the salt in your diet. Ideally you should have no more than 6 grams of salt a day. Most processed foods such as sauces, soups, crisps and other "nosh" are very high in salt, another reason why home cooking is healthier.

BARBECUED & FLAME-GRILLED MEAT

Barbecuing meat releases polycyclic aromatic hydrocarbons, which are carcinogens. The occasional barbecue is fine, particularly if it includes fresh vegetables, but avoid frequent barbecues or charcoal-grilled meat sizzlers, especially if the meat is blackened.

PROCESSED MEAT & ULTRA-PROCESSED FOOD

A study from the Sorbonne University in Paris looked at over 100,000 adults and followed them for 16 years. It found that a 10% increase in ultra-processed foods, such as factory-made pizza, biscuits, cakes, processed meats, and margarine were linked with a 12% increase in cancer including breast cancer.

Processed meats such as sausages, worscht, salami, and salt beef are unhealthy because their high fat and salt content, as well as the curing process, can render them carcinogenic. Smoked fish, including smoked salmon, has the usual benefits of oily fish but being smoked is less healthy and should be eaten in moderation. That said, a relatively high protein intake, by eating fresh fish, chicken, eggs, lentils, chickpeas, beans and nuts, may be cancer-protective.

ACRYLAMIDE

Some studies suggest that acrylamide, formed when manufacturing carbohydrate-rich snacks such as potato crisps, biscuits and frozen chips, may act as a weak carcinogen. It may also be produced when vegetables are roasted until they are charred at the edges. If you're roasting, grilling or barbecuing veggies, it's a good idea to stop cooking them once they turn golden brown.

ALCOHOL & COFFEE

Drinking alcohol heavily and frequently is a risk for several types of cancer. In contrast, coffee is protective against liver cancer, probably due to the antioxidants.

CASE STUDY

RECOVERING FROM CANCER

Deborah has always had a healthy life-style, eating well and exercising regularly. She has never smoked. She is an optimist with great self-confidence, enjoying nothing better than helping other people. So when she developed breast cancer in her fifties, it hit her hard. It felt undeserved, but she realised it was not her fault.

After the initial shock, and while recovering from surgery, she decided to make some lifestyle changes. Her diet was good but not perfect. She started eating more purple antioxidant-rich foods like aubergines, plums, and pomegranates, as well as lots of cruciferous vegetables. Natural yoghurt, beans, and flax seeds all made their way into her daily diet, along with intermittent fasting under the supervision of her doctor.

Aware that exercise was an important part of her recovery, she went back to playing golf and started going to the gym. She also found a relaxation and meditation class run by a charity that specialised in helping those affected by cancer. Debbie has regained her confidence and sense of control. She's looking forward to the future with renewed positivity and optimism.

OLD FLOUR & OATS

Maimonides recommended that one always use fresh, whole grain flour. We now know that whole grains can reduce the risk of cancer, but that old and mouldy wheat, oats, legumes, and other grains can be contaminated with aflatoxins, which are classified as carcinogenic by the International Agency for Research on Cancer (IARC). Mould in flour may not be visible, so pay attention to "use by" dates.

CANCER & COOKING

It is common to feel tired much of the time and experience loss of appetite while undergoing treatment for cancer. Eating little and often may be more manageable than sitting down to a regular lunch or dinner. Bear this in mind if you are cooking for someone with cancer. Organising a drop-off meal rota for them and their family can also be much appreciated.

If the person being treated for cancer is doing the cooking, taking short cuts like buying pre-chopped fruit and veg, nutritious ready meals, and ordering groceries online all save time and energy. On more energetic days, making a batch of soup or other tasty treats for the freezer can be both practical and life-affirming.

THINKING AHEAD

Emerging research suggests that boosting good gut bacteria by eating probiotics such as live natural yoghurt, kefir or sauerkraut, and prebiotics including artichokes, leeks, onions, and prunes, may help prevent cancer by supporting the immune system.

Evidence is also emerging that asparagine, found in asparagus, and to a lesser extent in protein-rich foods such as meat, fish, and eggs, may play a role in the spread of cancer. Asparagine is present in so many foods it is virtually impossible to avoid it, however, therapies to counteract its effects are currently being developed. For the time being, if you are a cancer survivor, you may wish to avoid eating asparagus on a regular basis.

FAMILY HISTORY

If you have a strong family history of cancer, either a first-degree relative who was affected at a young age, or a close relative with more than one type of cancer, you may want to talk to your doctor about attending a family history clinic for predictive genetic testing. Cancer research is one of the most rapidly evolving fields in medical research, with new drugs, discoveries, and therapies being developed all the time.

TO REDUCE YOUR RISK OF CANCER

* Avoid being overweight

* Eat more fruit and vegetables, especially cabbage and broccoli

* Add fibre such as milled flaxseed to your food

* Use extra virgin olive oil and omega-3 -rich foods

* Eat more fermented foods

* Embrace a vegetarian, vegan, or pescatarian diet

* Get plenty of vitamin D from sunlight and food and take supplements if advised

* Exercise for two and a half hours a week

* Try intermittent fasting, such as the Two-Day Diet

* Avoid deep-fried food and don't re-use frying oil

* Avoid processed and char-grilled meat, and all ultra-processed food

* Avoid sugary food and drinks

ALLERGIES, INTOLERANCES & GLUTEN-FREE DIETS

Some studies suggest that avoiding gluten may reduce the risk of allergies and autoimmune diseases, but more research is needed. A growing number of people are now following a gluten-free diet and tend to fall into three categories – those who have been diagnosed with coeliac disease and must not eat any gluten at all; those with non-coeliac gluten sensitivity who experience milder but regular reactions to eating gluten so prefer to avoid it; and those with no obvious symptoms but who have read about gluten-free diets and assume they must be healthier for everyone.

COELIAC DISEASE

Coeliac disease is an autoimmune illness that affects about one in a hundred people, slightly more among Ashkenazi Jews. Coeliac sufferers cannot tolerate foods that contain gluten, a protein found in wheat and rye and some other grains. Even very small amounts of gluten can cause problems such as headaches, abdominal discomfort, rash or digestive symptoms. If you experience these symptoms, it is important to get a proper diagnosis, so ask your GP about a coeliac disease blood test or endoscopy. In the short term, untreated coeliac disease can cause anaemia and vitamin deficiency, and in the long term, an increased chance of brittle bones and small bowel lymphoma, a type of cancer. Keeping strictly to a gluten-free diet greatly reduces these risks.

NON-COELIAC GLUTEN SENSITIVITY

Some people have similar symptoms to those with coeliac disease, such as bloating, tiredness, and headache, but their medical tests show normal results. If these symptoms are frequent and they feel generally unwell, it can be helpful to try a gluten-free diet with the support of a dietician. They can recommend suitable meal plans and offer advice on gluten-free grains such as amaranth, quinoa and gluten-free oats to ensure a good supply of essential nutrients such as B vitamins and folic acid. Many GF products are highly processed, so the best GF diets are based on fresh home-cooked foods. People who do not need to go fully gluten-free may find sourdough bread easier to digest than other breads as it contains lower levels of gluten.

FOOD ALLERGIES & INTOLERANCES

Food allergies are often diagnosed in childhood. Allergy to cow's milk can become apparent because of rash, diarrhoea, and colic and sometimes wheezing, but there can be other explanations, such as eczema and viral infection, so it is best to ask for an assessment by a health professional.

Much rarer are severe allergies to a specific food, most commonly nuts, sesame, or seafood. When exposed to problem foods, people at risk can suffer anaphylaxis, a life-threatening combination of breathing difficulties, collapse, and often a nettle-like rash. If you ever witness these symptoms, help them use their adrenaline injector pen (EpiPen) if they have one, and call an ambulance.

Food intolerances are less serious than allergies. Symptoms, which include bloating, tiredness, moodiness, or feeling tense or hyperactive, may be uncomfortable but are not life-threatening. The reaction often comes on slowly, some time after eating the problem food or drink, and even then only after consuming a fairly large amount of it.

Some people are intolerant to milk, suffering from headaches and digestive disorders. The intolerance can be due to cow's milk protein (A1 casein), in which case symptoms may improve by switching to A2 milk or goats' milk. Intolerance to food colouring artificial sweeteners, or monosodium glutamate (MSG) is also fairly common.

Determining which food is responsible for your symptoms usually takes time and detective work. First steps may include avoiding processed food and buying organic produce. Sometimes an intolerance is temporary, and after several months of abstinence, the problem food or drink can be reintroduced gradually. When it comes to food allergies, however, be extremely cautious, and seek professional advice.

* People with coeliac disease must avoid all food containing gluten

* Non-coeliac gluten sensitivity is an intolerance to gluten that does not show up in blood tests

* Symptoms of both coeliac disease and non-coeliac gluten sensitivity include headaches, fatigue, bloating, and other digestive symptoms

* A food allergy may cause a rash, wheezing, and more rarely, anaphylaxis

* A dietician or nutritionist can help find the cause of a food allergy or intolerance

INFLAMMATION & IBD

If the tissues are damaged by infection, injury, even by unhealthy food or additives, your body uses its immune system for healing. If this continues over an extended period, over-activity of the immune system can lead to inflammatory diseases such as rheumatoid arthritis, ulcerative colitis and Crohn's disease. Reducing inflammation is also important in the treatment of angina and Alzheimer's disease.

HERBS & SPICES

Research into the relationship between food and inflammation is relatively new, but some herbs and spices have been used for thousands of years to treat inflammation. Turmeric, used in traditional medicines; horseradish, a key ingredient in chrane, a much-loved Jewish accompaniment to fish balls; and wasabi, or Japanese horseradish, are all excellent anti-inflammatories.

Spices are often added to our food to enhance their flavour, but they also offer significant health benefits. One study in which common spices were added to inflammatory cells in lab cultures, showed they were good at calming inflammation.

Blood tests on people who eat a Mediterranean diet, which includes a liberal use of herbs, tend to show reduced markers of inflammation. Herbs with an anti-inflammatory effect include those in the mint family: sage, rosemary, thyme, basil, and oregano, which all contain an antioxidant called rosmarinic acid.

FRUIT & VEGETABLES

Many fruits and vegetables have an anti-inflammatory effect, probably due to their high levels of vitamins such as A, C and E and antioxidants including anthocyanins, found in purple foods. Cruciferous vegetables, including cabbage and cauliflower; quercetin, found in onions and apples; and selenium, found in mushrooms, fish and Brazil nuts can all help to dampen down inflammation.

GARLIC

Garlic has a special role in helping to reduce inflammation and infections. It contains allicin, a chemical with anti-viral properties, as well as selenium and glucosinolates. Studies have shown that regularly taking garlic or garlic supplements can significantly reduce your risk of catching a cold or other virus.

HEALTHY OILS & NUTS

Extra virgin olive oil and omega-3, supplying high levels of vitamin E and polyphenols, are anti-inflammatory. Omega-3 fats have been shown in several studies to improve the symptoms of rheumatoid arthritis. Frying can destroy the omega-3 in fish, so try to bake, poach, or microwave it instead. Frying also appears to increase inflammation, but this depends on the oil used and whether it is fresh and cold-pressed, or previously used and refined. Nuts and seeds contain healthy fats as well as zinc, which clears inflamed skin and aids wound healing. Almonds and pumpkin seeds are rich in magnesium, which also has anti-inflammatory properties.

GUT BACTERIA & INFLAMMATION

Our gut bacteria have a key role in helping us to have a healthy immune system, essential to avoid inflammation. Fermented and high fibre foods can help good gut bacteria thrive and so raise immunity. These also help to maintain the intestinal barrier, reducing the risk of inflammation of the bowel and preventing a condition known as leaky gut, which plays a role in food allergies and autoimmune disorders.

Other foods are harmful to our good gut bacteria or allow unhealthy strains to grow. These include sugar and other refined carbohydrates, alcohol, processed foods containing certain preservatives, and pesticides. Artificial sweeteners, such as aspartame and sucralose, appear likely to have a similar effect. Red meat and chicken, especially if processed, can cause inflammation, another reason not to eat red meat every day. A semi-vegetarian diet with plenty of vegetables in which meat is eaten only once a fortnight and fish once or twice a week, appears to reduce the recurrence of inflammatory bowel disease.

Processed foods, especially those containing emulsifiers like carageenan and xanthan gum (often used in margarine, shop-bought mayonnaise, ice cream, and some milk substitutes) may damage the bowel wall and are a risk for inflammation. Other additives such as maltodextrin, or modified starch, used in cakes and biscuits, or traces of fertilisers and pesticides in non-organic produce, may have similar effects.

FOOD INTOLERANCES & INFLAMMATION

Some people find that joint pains or swelling are improved by excluding certain foods such as gluten or lactose from their diet. Others may respond to a low carb diet. Less commonly, eliminating members of the nightshade family such as aubergines, tomatoes and potatoes can alleviate symptoms. All these exclusion diets should be with the help of a dietician. Ben Brown, author of The Digestive Health Solution recommends adding more whole foods, fermented foods and prebiotics to your diet, and avoiding processed foods to see if this alleviates symptoms before considering an exclusion diet.

IBS, ULCERATIVE COLITIS, & CROHN'S DISEASE

IBS (irritable bowel syndrome) is a condition associated with spasm of the bowel wall and abdominal pain. Ulcerative colitis and Crohn's disease are autoimmune conditions, together known as inflammatory bowel disease (IBD). Ashkenazi Jews unfortunately have a relatively high incidence of these illnesses. One small but detailed study on forty patients with IBD, found that persevering with an anti-inflammatory diet led to improved symptoms. Probiotics and prebiotics also protect against IBD.

Whole grains and dairy products work with your good bacteria to form butyrate, a compound that helps to heal the bowel wall. However, some patients with IBD find their symptoms are reduced if they avoid dairy products. Professor Arie Levine of the Wolfson Medical Institute in Israel, is currently investigating restrictive diets for people with IBD, and has had promising early results.

ANTI-INFLAMMATORY DIETS

THE IBD-AID DIET

The Inflammatory Bowel Disease Anti-Inflammatory Diet is low in lactose and in refined carbohydrates and red meat, but high in prebiotics and probiotics, olive oil, omega-3, and coconut oil. It has helped some patients achieve remission, or reduce their medications.

PERSONALISED EXCLUSION DIETS

Participants follow a very limited diet for several weeks. Once there is evidence of healing, individual foods are carefully re-introduced with the support of a dietician.

THE LOW FODMAP DIET

Originally designed to treat irritable bowel syndrome, this low carb diet excludes certain fruit and vegetables, xylitol, erythritol, lactose, wheat, and prebiotics, and can relieve some symptoms of IBD. However, it can also reduce the diversity of good gut bacteria, so it is important carefully to re-introduce those foods that do not cause symptoms.

THE SPECIFIC CARBOHYDRATE DIET

The SCD is a very restrictive diet that avoids most refined sugars, fibre, and starches, but encourages consumption of probiotics like bio yoghurt and kefir. There have been good results in some patients with severe IBD, however, they miss out on the benefits of fibre.

ANTI-INFLAMMATORY FOODS

* Fruit and cruciferous vegetables
* Garlic
* Healthy fats
* Herbs
* Horseradish
* Nuts
* Probiotics and prebiotics
* Spices

INFLAMMATION-CAUSING FOODS

* Alcohol
* Artificial additives & preservatives
* Deep-fried foods
* Emulsifying agents
* Excess salt
* Gluten and dairy - if allergic or intolerant
* Processed meat
* Red meat
* Refined omega-6 fats
* Sugar & white carbs
* Trans fats

A HEALTHY RELATIONSHIP WITH FOOD

Learning to appreciate one's body with all its imperfections is an important part of developing a healthy relationship with what you eat. Try not to feel upset or angry with yourself after a lapse or binge, and return to the usual healthy eating pattern afterwards. Over-eating on a single day, unless this is happening repeatedly, will not cause lasting weight-gain but may make you feel over-full and uncomfortable and retain some water, so the scales may appear to show weight-gain. Keeping healthy snacks at hand, and staying out of the kitchen when not preparing meals, may help.

Some people decide to restrict their diet without being advised to do so, going gluten or dairy-free, or by switching from regular milk to sweetened almond or soy milk, in spite of their high sugar content. This can cause stress and may have been unnecessary. It is possible to get vitamin deficiencies if you are excluding whole food groups without professional advice.

We hope that healthy eating becomes second nature, leading to feelings of improved wellbeing, free from anxieties around food choices. Occasionally people can become obsessed with their diet and so-called "clean eating", even when they are physically healthy with no allergies or intolerances. This may make them feel anxious or stressed, sometimes causing them to refuse invitations to social events for fear of being served "unhealthy" food.

Obsession with diet that is affecting a person in such a negative way is known as orthorexia. It is common for people with orthorexia to exercise to excess. Sometimes all that is necessary is to recognise what is happening, not worry about the occasional treat, and reduce the intensity of exercising. If it is affecting their ability to socialise, or causing them to feel upset or depressed, it is wise to talk to a GP who may refer them to a counsellor or psychotherapist. The orthorexia may be a symptom of underlying emotional difficulties.

Bulimia and anorexia nervosa are more extreme eating disorders, often with underlying psychological problems. If binge eating, weight can fluctuate greatly, and if fasting, can drop too rapidly. In either case, it's important to seek medical or psychological help as soon as possible.

* Orthorexia is a condition where eating healthily and exercising become obsessional

* It is important not to allow anxieties around food to isolate you

* People should go easy on themselves and not expect perfection

A HEALTHY PREGNANCY

EATING FOR TWO?

Before a planned pregnancy, it's important to aim for as healthy a weight as possible. Being over-weight can reduce fertility; during pregnancy, it increases the risk of complications like diabetes, and doubles the chance of needing a Caesarean section. It also makes it harder to lose weight afterwards, leading to more and more weight gain with each pregnancy.

A low carb diet before pregnancy may help, however, its safety during pregnancy is not yet known. During pregnancy, it's essential to eat protein, healthy fats, whole grains, and foods rich in vitamins such as fruit and vegetables. It may also be helpful to eat frequent smaller meals throughout the day to maintain a steady blood sugar level. Food that is high in fibre, and complex carbohydrates such as wholegrain bread, oatcakes, nuts, and seeds, can also be helpful.

In the early weeks, an expectant mother may experience nausea and her appetite may be poor. One easy remedy is drinking hot water infused with fresh mint leaves or slices of ginger.

It is important not to overeat during pregnancy and to minimise refined carbohydrates, sugar, and processed snacks. In the first trimester, the mother needs no extra calories, and by the last weeks of the pregnancy, her need for calories goes up by only 200-300 kcal a day. That said, dieting while pregnant is not recommended and may damage the health of both mother and baby.

FOLIC ACID

To reduce the risk of spina bifida in the baby, getting enough folic acid is essential, especially in the first trimester. Green leafy vegetables help, but to ensure an adequate intake it is safest to take folic acid tablets. It's best to start taking these when pregnancy is planned, or as soon as a woman learns she is pregnant. The recommended dosage varies according to circumstances, and needs to be discussed with a doctor or pharmacist.

EAT FISH, BUT NOT TOO MUCH

Oily fish is good to eat in moderation, about twice a week. It should be fresh and well cooked, so avoid raw fish and sushi. Tuna should not be eaten more than once a month because it may contain small amounts of mercury. Fish, milk, and strawberries also provide iodine for thyroid health and to support the baby's growth and brain development.

Omega-3 from oily fish can help the development of the baby's brain, and reduces the risk of preterm birth. If the mother is vegetarian, she can take algae oil instead. Omega-3 has also been shown to reduce the incidence of asthma and wheezing in the infant, and reduce anxiety and depression in the mother. The expectant mum should also limit her intake of refined oils such as sunflower oil, getting the omega-6 she needs from nuts, seeds, eggs, and milk.

VITAMINS, MINERALS & SUPPLEMENTS

Key supplements in pregnancy are iron, folic acid, vitamin D, and omega-3. NHS Healthy Start vouchers, available to some expectant mothers, can be used for free milk, fruit, vegetables, and vitamins. Taking excess vitamin supplements during pregnancy may do more harm than good. For example, too much vitamin A can be a risk for miscarriage.

Choline is important for development of the baby's brain and spinal cord. Eggs are a good source, as are fish, such as salmon, cauliflower and broccoli.

Many pregnant women have iron deficiency, which causes them to feel tired, dizzy, or breathless. Red meat, chicken, fish, dairy products, dark green leafy vegetables such as spinach, whole grains, and legumes are all good sources of iron. It is better absorbed if these foods are taken with vitamin C, in citrus fruit for example. Many women also need iron supplements, especially if they are vegetarian or vegan.

Vitamin D is essential for a healthy pregnancy. For the baby, it promotes strong bones and teeth, improves growth, and reduces the risk of premature birth. It also lowers the risk of infection in both mother and baby. Research suggests vitamin D may also reduce the risk of asthma and wheeze in the infant. See also page 234.

AVOIDING INFECTIONS

Food poisoning, although rare, can be a risk for miscarriage, so good hygiene, such as frequent hand washing, when preparing food is essential. When possible, buy organic fruits and vegetables, and peel or wash them well to remove traces of soil, which can help avoid toxoplasmosis, which can cause miscarriage. Eggs should be stamped with the British Lion Mark to ensure the chickens have been vaccinated against salmonella. Raw eggs, in homemade mousse or mayonnaise, for example, are best avoided.

It's important to avoid cross-contamination by keeping raw and cooked meat and poultry well away from each other. Store raw meat in a separate part of the fridge so no juices can drip onto other food, and use separate chopping boards for raw and cooked meats. All meat and poultry should be fresh and well cooked throughout, with no pink or red visible.

Unpasteurised milk and soft cheeses such as Camembert and Brie can be a risk for listeria, so it is best to avoid all soft cheeses with a white rind, including goats' cheese, as well as soft blue cheese. Hard and cooked cheeses are generally safe in pregnancy.

A word of caution for cat-owners and gardeners: cats can carry toxoplasmosis, as may soil, so always wear gloves when changing the litter tray or gardening, and wash your hands afterwards.

OTHER FOODS TO AVOID

Liver is rich in vitamin A, which in high doses can increase the risk of miscarriage. It is best to avoid trans fats (partially hydrogenated oils), food additives, aspartame, acesulfame potassium, monosodium glutamate, hydrolysed vegetable protein, high fructose corn syrup, and any food with E numbers, such as edible dyes. Regularly drinking sugary sodas and diet sodas may significantly increase the risk of preterm birth, but reducing sugar can lower the risk of obesity in the baby, even into adult life. Minimising alcohol for the duration of the pregnancy, and not smoking also give the baby the best chance of long term health.

BREASTFEEDING

Breast milk gives a young baby a very good start in life, providing all the nutrients it needs. It provides antibodies and good bacteria, helping the child have fewer infections and fight them off more quickly. A child who has been breastfed is less likely to suffer from obesity, diabetes, or heart disease as an adult. The mother benefits too, by improved bonding with the baby, and losing the extra weight gained in pregnancy. Breastfeeding also reduces her risk of breast or ovarian cancer later in life. The longer she can breastfeed her baby, the better the protection.

Most of the advice on what to eat during pregnancy is the same as when breastfeeding. Omega-3 is still important for baby's brain development, vitamin D for healthy bones and teeth. One study showed that when a mother who breastfeeds drinks organic milk, her baby is less likely to suffer from eczema. Many new mothers are low in iron, and topping this up can reduce tiredness, however, folic acid supplements are no longer needed once breastfeeding.

FASTING

Most rabbis recommend that breastfeeding and pregnant mothers do not observe religious fasts. Fasting can increase the risk of fainting and may reduce the supply of nutrients to the baby. It is generally safe to eat light meals and drink only water on religious fast days.

A HEALTHY PREGNANCY

* All women planning to become pregnant should take folic acid supplements

* Iron-rich food, including meat, fish, greens, whole grains, and pulses, are essential during pregnancy

* Omega-3 and iodine support development of the baby's brain

* Pregnant women should take a low dose vitamin D supplement

* Milk, hard cheese, soy, and sardines are high in calcium for healthy bones and teeth

* To avoid infections, meat and poultry should be very fresh and thoroughly cooked

* Avoid liver, chopped or otherwise, raw eggs or egg whites, and soft cheeses

* Avoid over-eating. In the last three months of pregnancy, calorie intake only needs to increase by 15%

FOOD & MOOD

Food has always been a central part of Jewish life, bringing family and friends together. What we eat affects not only our physical wellbeing but also our mood and mental health, so this is surely the way to end a book on healthy Jewish food.

The Predimed Study looked at the impact of the Mediterranean diet on reducing the risk of heart disease, but researchers also discovered it reduced the risk of depression by 30%, showing that health and happiness are intricately linked.

The Australian Smiles Trial showed that patients with moderate to severe depression improved through regular meetings with nutritionists, and following a Mediterranean-style diet, a great example of diet and medical treatment working in tandem.

CAFFEINE & ALCOHOL

Caffeine can cause anxiety symptoms and insomnia. Some people are particularly sensitive to its effects so cutting down on tea, coffee, cola, and chocolate can help them feel calmer and sleep better. Many of the patients I see who are suffering from severe anxiety turn out to be heavy drinkers. An alcoholic drink may briefly lift your mood at the time, but regularly drinking alcohol other than in small quantities is likely to make you feel anxious or irritable. Alcohol also interferes with the action of omega-3 and melatonin, the sleep cycle hormone, so regular drinkers are often prone to insomnia.

VITAMIN D DEFICIENCY

When your vitamin D level is low, your mood falls and you feel aches and pains. Diet can help restore vitamin D, but is not as effective as sunlight. It is good to take a 10 to 15 minute walk in the late morning each day, even in winter. You are likely to return to your tasks feeling more energetic and better able to concentrate, and might also find you sleep better (see page 234).

ADDITIVES

People vary in which foods disagree with them, but certain additives used in processed foods have a reputation for adversely affecting mood and energy. These include tartrazine (E102), monosodium glutamate (MSG or E621), aspartame (used as a sweetener in many diet drinks), and benzoic acid (E210). In some people, these cause depression, anxiety, insomnia, poor concentration, and headaches.

FOODS FOR HAPPINESS

There is good evidence that certain foods contribute to happiness and a sense of wellbeing. Tryptophan, found in meat, poultry, cheese, and nuts – especially almonds and peanuts – plays a major role in helping the brain synthesise serotonin, a neurotransmitter that can lift mood. Foods rich in tryptophan are most beneficial when eaten with complex carbohydrates such as whole grains. Tryptophan also produces melatonin, lack of which is known to cause symptoms of depression.

Vitamin B3 (niacin) found in meat, fish, eggs, yeast, and whole grains is closely related to tryptophan, and Vitamin C helps convert tryptophan to serotonin.

Omega-3 is important for the formation of brain cell membranes. When these are healthy, mood enhancing neurotransmitters such as serotonin, are more effective. Fish or algae oil are the most efficient sources.

Herbs can also make you happier. Chamomile tea is often taken to help people sleep, and is good at settling anxiety. As the name suggests, lemon balm can also have a calming effect, as do other members of the mint family, including peppermint, rosemary, and marjoram.

EATING FOR HAPPINESS

* A low carb diet can ease anxiety

* Tryptophan from poultry, cheese, and nuts can lift your mood

* Whole grains help boost tryptophan levels

* Omega-3 and ahiflower oil counteract depression

* Drinking less alcohol reduces anxiety and negative thoughts

* If you are vitamin D deficient, a supplement can lift your mood

* The Mediterranean diet keeps you healthy in both mind and body

AND FINALLY,

To bring things full circle, it is the Mediterranean diet that once again excels, providing a mix of vitamins, minerals, and healthy fats that help promote emotional wellbeing.

On that note, Judi and I wish you happiness, health, and as the old saying goes, may you live to be a hundred and twenty.

L'CHAIM – TO LIFE!

SELECTED BIBLIOGRAPHY

BOOKS*

30-Second Nutrition: The 50 Most Significant
Food-related Facts, Each Explained in Half
a Minute
Professor Julie A Lovegrove, Ivy Press 2018

Beating Stress, Anxiety and Depression:
Groundbreaking Ways to Help You Feel Better
Professor Jane Plant and Janet Stephenson,
Piatkus 2011

Diet of the Mind: The Latest Science on
What to Eat to Prevent Alzheimer's and
Cognitive Decline
Dr Martha Morris, Macmillan 2017

Eat Fat Get Thin: Why the Fat We Eat is the Key
to Sustained Weight Loss and Vibrant Health
Dr Mark Hyman, Hodder and Stoughton, 2016

Emotional Intelligence: Why it Can Matter
More Than IQ
Daniel Goleman, Bloomsbury 1996

Fat Chance: The Hidden Truth About Sugar,
Obesity and Disease
Professor Robert Lustig, Fourth Estate 2013

Gut: The Inside Story of Our Body's Most
Under-rated Organ
Giulia Enders, Scribe UK 2015

Reverse Your Diabetes: The Step-by-Step Plan
to Take Control of Type 2 Diabetes
Dr David Cavan, Vermilion 2014

The 8 Week Blood Sugar Diet: Lose Weight Fast
and Reprogramme Your Body
Dr Michael Mosley, Short Books 2015

The Compassionate Mind
Paul Gilbert, Constable & Robinson 2009

The Diet Myth: The Real Science Behind
What We Eat
Professor Tim Spector, Weidenfeld & Nicolson
2015

The Digestive Health Solution:
Your Personalised Plan for Inside Out
Digestive Wellness
Benjamin I Brown, Exisle Publishing 2015

The End of Alzheimer's
Dale Bredeson, Vermilion 2017

The Four Pillar Plan: How to Relax, Eat, Move
and Sleep Your Way to a Longer, Healthier Life
Dr Rangan Chatterjee, Penguin 2017

The Life of Riley: Mastering the Five Secret
Habits to Enjoy a Longer and Healthier Life
Phil Riley, Columbus Publishing 2016

The Royal Marsden Cancer Cookbook:
Nutritious Recipes for During and After
Cancer Treatment
Clare Shaw, Kyle Books 2015

The Two Day Diet: The Original,
Bestselling 5:2 Diet
Dr Michelle Harvie and Professor Tony Howell,
Penguin 2019

They Are What You Feed Them: How Food
Can Improve Your Child's Behaviour, Learning
and Mood
Dr Alex Richardson, HarperNonFiction 2010

* May contain references to non-kosher ingredients

ARTICLES*

ALCOHOL

Moderate alcohol consumption as risk factor for adverse brain outcomes and cognitive decline: longitudinal cohort study
Allan CL et al, BMJ 2017:357:j2353

CANCER

Consumption of ultra-processed foods and cancer risk: results from NutriNet-Santé prospective cohort
Stour B et al, BMJ 2018;360:K322

Nutrition and cancer: a review of the evidence for an anti-cancer diet
Michael S Donaldson, Nutrition Journal 11 (2004) 3:19/ DOI:10.1186/1475-2891-3-19

CHOLESTEROL AND FAT

Consumption of fried foods and risk of coronary heart disease: Spanish cohort of the European Prospective Investigation into Cancer and Nutrition Study
Guallar-Castillon et al, BMJ 2012; 344: e363

Milk and dairy produce and CVD: new perspectives on dairy and cardiovascular Health
Lovegrove J and Hobbs D, Univ Reading, Proceedings of the Nutrition Society (2016)
75, 247-258

Dietary intake of saturated fat by food source and incident cardiovascular disease: the Multi-Ethnic Study of Atherosclerosis
Mozaffarian D et al, Am J Clin Nutr. 2012 Aug; 96 (2) 397-404

DEMENTIA

The role of nutrition on cognition and brain health in ageing: a targeted approach
Cohen NJ et al, Univ of Illinois, Nutrition Research Reviews, (2015) 28, 167-180

Impact of diet on adult hippocampal neurogenesis
Stangl D and Thuret S, Genes Nutr. 2009, Dec, 4 (4) 271-282

The MIND Diet: Fighting Dementia with Food
Judith C Thalheimer, Today's Geriatric Medicine, Vol 8, No 4, 10

DIABETES

Evidence-based nutrition guidelines for prevention and management of diabetes
Diabetes UK, March 2018

Low carbohydrate diet to achieve weight loss and improve HbA1c in type 2 diabetes and pre-diabetes: Experience from one general practice
Unwin D, Practical Diabetes, 2014, Vol 31, No 2

Prevention and management of type 2 diabetes: dietary components and nutritional strategies
Hamdy O et al, Lancet Vol 383, Issue 9933, 7-13 June 2014,1999-2007

HYPERTENSION

Effects of the dietary approaches to stop hypertension diet alone and in combination with exercise and calorie restriction on insulin sensitivity and lipids
Blumenthal JA et al, Hypertension 2010, May 55(5)1199-1205

Perspectives of the public on reducing the population salt intake in Ireland
McConnon A et al, Public Health Nutrition, 2016,19(7)1327-1335

HEART DISEASE

Prospective association of the Mediterranean diet with cardiovascular disease incidence and mortality and its population impact in a mon-Mediterranean population: the EPIC-Norfolk Study
Forouhi et al, BMC Medicine 2016, 14:135

Unprocessed Red and Processed Meats
and Risk of Coronary Artery Disease
and Type 2 Diabetes Mellitus
Mozaffarian D et al, Curr Atheroscl. Rep 2012, Dec 14
(6) p515-524

Fruit and vegetable intake and mortality
from ischaemic heart disease: results
from the European Prospective Investigation
into Cancer and Nutrition (EPIC) – Heart Study
Appleby P et al, European
Heart Journal, 2011, Vol 32, Issue 10, 1235-1243

INFLAMMATION, INCLUDING CROHN'S DISEASE

Anti-inflammatory activity of extracts from fruits, herbs
and spices
Hobiger S et al, Food Chemistry (2010) 122, 987-996

The evolving role of diet in the pathology
and treatment of IBD
BMJ Gut, Arie Levine, 2018, Sep; 67 (9):1726-1738

MOOD

A randomised controlled trial of dietary improvement
for adults with major depression
(the SMILES trial)
Berk M et al, BMC Medicine 2017;15:23

Adherence to Mediterranean diet and risk
of depression later in life. A cross-sectional
study in East Attica, Greece
K Argyropoulos, Sciendo, 22 Aug 2019, Vol 2,
Issue 2, p201-209

EXERCISE

Objectively Measured Daily Steps and Subsequent
Long Term All-Cause Mortality: the Tasped
Prospective Cohort Study
Blair S et al, PLOS One. 2015; 10 (11)

*See healthyjewishcookery.wordpress.com
for full bibliography

INDEX

ACKNOWLEDGEMENTS

So many people have made this project possible. Special thanks to our incredibly talented designer and stylist, Pene Parker, Marc Gerstein for his gorgeous photography, Grace Helmer for her beautiful illustrations, Professor Len Goldstone for his meticulous pre-editing, Eva Lasry-Dome for her nutritional input and expertise, and Pepi Eirew for her delightful cartoons.

Family and friends offered us suggestions, ideas and moral support, especially Marc and Jamie Gerstein, Alex Wiseman, Margaret Rose, David and Andrea Rose, Sarah Angel, Vicki Mercer, Dr Jane Shapiro, Laurence and Louise Blume, Sarah Dubov, Alan Freeman, Stuart Goodman, Sora Jaffe, Abi Hartuv, Sue Lewis, Anne Mark, Sima Raw, Sue Surkes, Sue Szuszkiewicz, and Sharon Tomlinson.

We're also indebted to the following medical and nutritional professionals
for their time and advice:

Dr Alex Richardson, Founder Director of Food and Behaviour
(FAB) Research, Oxford

Professor Robert Lustig, Professor of Paediatric Endocrinology,
University of California

Professor Ronald Krauss, Professor of Nutritional Science,
University of California

Professor Paul Addis, Professor Emeritus
of Food Science and Nutrition, University of Minnesota

Professor Philip Calder, Professor of Nutritional Immunology,
University of Southampton

Professor Gerald Krystal, Cancer Research Scientist,
University of British Columbia

Dr David Cavan, Director of Policy and Programmes,
The International Diabetes Federation

Dr Charlotte Evans, Lecturer in Nutrition,
University of Leeds

Dr Michelle Harvie, Nightingale and Genesis
Prevention Unit, Wythenshawe Hospital, Manchester

Elena Philippou, Assistant Professor of Nutrition, University of Nicosia

Dr David Unwin, pioneering GP, Southport

Carmel Burke, nutritionist

Jay Charara, psychologist

Jennifer Low, Ruth Parker,
and Judy Thalheimer, dieticians

THE AUTHORS

JUDI ROSE

Judi is the daughter of the legendary Evelyn Rose, and collaborated with her mother on numerous articles, recipes and cookbooks. After a career at the BBC as a science and technology producer, she followed in her mother's footsteps as a cookbook author, food writer and cookery teacher. Judi also runs the Cookery Studio, a culinary space in West London for cookery classes, events, and food photography.

JACKIE ROSE MbChB, MRCGP, DCH, DRCOG

Jackie worked as a GP for 27 years. Since 2014, she has developed a keen interest in healthy eating and preventative medicine, and is co-chair of Salford Healthy Communities advocating for the health of Orthodox Jews. To research this book she has liaised with leading nutritional experts in the USA, Canada and UK on dietary health, longevity and disease prevention. Dr Rose now works as a nutritionist at Private GP Extra in Greater Manchester.

PENE PARKER MA RCA

Pene is an award-winning London-based art director, designer and stylist. As creative director at BBC Worldwide, Pene worked on a wide variety of bestselling books and DVDs, including *Blue Planet* and later, while at Mitchell Beazley, she specialised in cookery-book design, creating many acclaimed titles, including those for The Ginger Pig. Pene continues to design cookery titles on a consultancy basis for many leading publishers including Square Peg, for whom she has art directed and designed the internationally bestselling *Roasting Tin* series. Pene also runs a prop-supply company and art directs and styles for magazines, commercials and films.

MARC GERSTEIN

Marc has been photographing since he was six years old. He studied photography under Minor White and Jonathan W. Green in MIT's Creative Photography program. His food photographs have appeared regularly in the Jewish Chronicle, while his portraits of Evelyn Rose and Judi Rose grace their book covers. Originally a New Yorker, Marc is now based in London.

PROFITS FROM TO LIFE! WILL BE SHARED WITH THESE CHARITIES

WORLD JEWISH RELIEF

In the 1930s we saved Jewish lives; now we save lives because we are Jewish. Driven by the values of loving-kindness, charity, and social justice, we strive to end poverty and help people recover from humanitarian crises worldwide.

worldjewishrelief.org

CHAI CANCER CARE

We provide professional services and support to any member of the Jewish community affected by cancer – patients, their families and friends, across the UK and internationally.

chaicancercare.org

SAVE A CHILD'S HEART

We mend hearts and save lives regardless of religion, gender or nationality by providing life-saving cardiac treatment to children from developing countries and training health care professionals to deliver quality care in their home communities.

saveachildsheart.org